Investigating STATISTICS

A BEGINNER'S GUIDE

ALAN GRAHAM

Hodder & Stoughton

LONDON SYDNEY AUCKLAND TORON

Contents

Foreword

The aim of this book is to provide a painless introduction to the key ideas of Statistics. The mystifying formulae of Statistics can be easily studied later when you have got from this book a good understanding of what such formulae are designed to measure.

It has been written for students beginning Statistics at B. Tec., sixth form and first year tertiary level. The latter includes universities and polytechnics, colleges of further and higher education, and colleges of education.

The growth of Statistics courses in these areas has been enormous in recent years and this book has been written to support the many non-expert teachers in need of a suitable textbook which both they and their students can understand.

USING THIS BOOK

ACTIVITIES

Throughout each chapter are a number of 'activities'. They are there to let you pause and consider the points being raised and to allow you to relate them to your own experiences. Although the comments follow in the text directly after each activity, please don't just skip over them; they really will help you to clarify your understanding of the statistical ideas in the book and to go on understanding them after you have put the book down.

EXERCISES

At the end of each chapter are a number of exercises. These will give you further practice at using the statistical ideas in that chapter and should also provide a source of interesting data which you might wish to investigate further.

ACKNOWLEDGEMENTS

Grateful thanks to Ken Tyler and Luke Graham for their support in writing this book.

1 _Introduction_

WHAT IS THE POINT OF LEARNING STATISTICS?

Not so long ago the subject Statistics tended to be thought of as a branch of Mathematics. As a result, it was often taught in a fairly abstract, formal way, using difficult calculations and formulae. More recently, however, Statistics has been recognised as being important in Social Science, Science and Humanities and in a wide variety of professions such as medicine, social work, engineering and so on. Many Statistics courses are now being taught to these non-specialist (statistically speaking) groups and although they are, to some extent, specially designed for a particular audience, these courses are all similar in one important respect. This is that they aim to get across to students several _key statistical ideas_ which are useful and important in all sorts of situations. These key ideas are outlined in the next section, but it should be helpful to give a general overview here.

Statistics provides a way of getting a handle on data. In our homes and work places we are faced with countless facts and figures. Perhaps the most basic statistical skill of all here is simple numeracy — being able to calculate averages, working comfortably with percentages, and so on. Sometimes statistical information is conjured up to support highly dubious arguments. Graphs can be deliberately drawn incorrectly and figures used selectively to 'prove' a point (for example in advertising). Fortunately, there are certain 'ground rules' for presenting statistical information and there are a few testing questions by which you can often turn someone else's hard facts into quivering jelly! If you have an understanding of what these key questions are — even only an intuitive grasp — then you are less likely to be 'conned' in the future. If you know something about how data can be displayed and the sort of patterns you can expect, then you will be alert to any jiggery pokery that might be at work.

Here is an example of this pattern spotting, taken from the ordinary everyday world of beer barrels.

A well-known beer manufacturer produces empty beer barrels to a particular specification. By law, the barrels must be at least 36 gallons. Clearly, not all the barrels turn out to be *exactly* the same size. So each barrel is measured and any with a capacity of less than 36 gallons is broken up. A statistician was employed to check over the results of this measuring process. Here are the first 40 results that she received.

Barrel	Capacity (gal)	Barrel	Capacity (gal)	Barrel	Capacity (gal)	Barrel	Capacity (gal)
1	36.5	11	37.2	21	37.5	31	36.8
2	38.7	12	34.6	22	33.4	32	34.0
3	37.2	13	36.5	23	36.5	33	39.1
4	36.0	14	38.5	24	37.4	34	36.9
5	36.2	15	36.3	25	36.1	35	37.5
6	34.7	16	36.3	26	38.6	36	36.1
7	36.7	17	36.4	27	36.6	37	36.4
8	36.1	18	34.4	28	37.2	38	37.4
9	37.3	19	36.6	29	36.1	39	36.5
0	36.2	20	36.2	30	36.2	40	36.2

Figure 1.1   The capacities of 40 beer barrels

She then graphed the data so that it looked something like this:

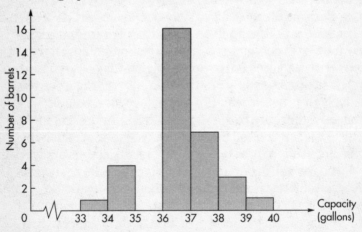

Figure 1.2   Data from figure 1.1 presented graphically

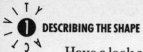

DESCRIBING THE SHAPE

Have a look at the shape of the block graph on page 2. Briefly describe its shape and explain why you think it looks like it does.

● **COMMENTS**

The statistician in question wasn't too surprised that the block graph peaked in the middle — this is a common feature. What did surprise her slightly was that there were no barrels in the 35–36 gallon range. She took a larger sample of results a few days later, which revealed the same thing. She decided to visit the section of the factory where the measurements took place and observe.

She found that the work was being carried out by two men, one of whom had the job of rolling the heavy reject barrels up a steep slope to be broken up by the other man as shown in figure 1.3.

Figure 1.3   Before the statistician's visit

Her solution to the 'problem' was to swap the positions of the two men round. Now the under-sized barrels were pushed gently down the slope to be broken up, as shown in figure 1.4.

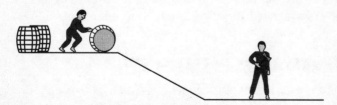

Figure 1.4   After the statistician's visit

Not surprisingly, the 'hole' in the block graph mysteriously disappeared in the next and subsequent batches!

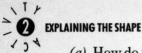

② EXPLAINING THE SHAPE

(a) How do you think the two men were falsifying the results and why?

(b) Why was it important to the beer company that the men should not falsify the results in this way?

(c) Draw a rough sketch of what the original block graph should have looked like.

(d) Where do you think the data which should have filled the 'hole' were actually recorded?

● **COMMENTS**

The statistician was fairly sure that the men were not recording correctly the capacities of the barrels which were just under the minimum capacity. So, any barrel which they measured as being between 35 and 36 gallons they put down as just over 36 gallons. The reason for this was clearly that they didn't enjoy rolling the heavy reject barrels up the slope. The problem for the beer company was that they were liable to prosecution if they were caught selling beer in under-sized barrels. The expected shape of the graph was a smooth curve with a peak in the middle, falling away to two tails on either side. Finally, the data which should have filled the 'hole' in the distribution were clearly being pushed to the right to be included in the 'just over 36 gallons' category.

This example, which is actually based on a true story, illustrates how a simple statistical idea (awareness of the 'shape' of a block graph) can help to identify and solve a practical problem. It also shows how little 'information' is revealed from a disorganised set of figures. The next section outlines some of the other important statistical ideas which will emerge throughout the rest of the book.

WHAT ARE THE KEY IDEAS IN STATISTICS?

You have already looked at one important statistical concept — the idea of 'shape' of a set of figures when they are arranged in sequence and then grouped together. Statistics generally involves collecting some facts and figures — usually called *data*. The data might be collected by *counting* (for example in a traffic survey where you want to count the number of cars, lorries, etc.).

Alternatively, data may be collected by *measuring* something. For example in the case of the beer barrels, the capacity of each barrel had to be measured.

When we measure things (for example, people's heights or the weights of bags of sugar, there is, inevitably, some *variation*. This might be because the things being measured have obviously different values (as with people's heights). Alternatively it could be that, although the measurements are supposed to be all the same, there is some degree of variation due to measuring inaccuracies. For example, if you weighed the same bag of sugar accurately on different scales, they would all show slightly different weights.

When we wish to see a clearer pattern in the measurements it is useful to graph them. Here the variation in the data will show up in the spread of the graph. A more general word for the overall shape of the graph is its *distribution*. The beer barrels example provides a good illustration of this notion of distribution. If you look again at figure 1.2, you will see a fairly typical picture of what distributions often look like, with a peak in the middle and the two tails dropping off to either side. In simple terms, this can be described by saying that quite a lot of the barrels fall into the middle of the range (this is the central peak), with only a few being extremely large or extremely small (these are the tails at either side).

Sometimes we need to know whether one group (often called a *population*) of people or things are richer, bigger, longer-lasting, . . ., than another group. For example, you might be gripped by the popular obsession of whether your wash is as white as it might be. Should you change to Brand X? Well, in the world of TV advertisements, one housewife gives her own opinion as to which brand is better, and we are expected to take her word for it. But for the more important questions in life (that's not to say that getting a whiter wash isn't important, however!) we may wish to base our decision on more than the experience of just one person. The usual 'statistical' approach is to take *samples* from each group, measure all the items in each sample, and then compare them. For obvious reasons, this procedure is known as *sampling*.

When two samples have been taken and the data collected, the next problem is to make a comparison and decide between them. However, because of natural variation (mentioned above), you can't expect different samples taken from the same population to be exactly the same. This makes it difficult to be sure that the samples you have taken are fair ones. For example, suppose you wished to compare the speed of delivery of first class and second class post. A simple statistical approach to tackling this problem has been carried out and the stages of this investigation are set out below. Read them through and then try to answer the question in Activity 3.

PROBLEM   Is the first class post faster than the second class post?

SOLUTION

Stage 1   Collect the data
Choose a sample of five letters posted first class and a sample of five posted second class and see how long each letter took to be delivered.

Type of letter	Days taken for delivery
First class letters	1, 1, 1, 2, 1
Second class letters	1, 3, 2, 2, 1

Stage 2   Analyse the data
The next step might be to calculate the average number of days for each sample and compare the two averages, thus:

First class average $= \dfrac{1+1+1+2+1}{5} = 1.2$ days

Second class average $= \dfrac{1+3+2+2+1}{5} = 1.8$ days

Stage 3   Interpret the results
Clearly the first class average is less than the second class average, so this proves that the first class post is faster.

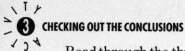

3 CHECKING OUT THE CONCLUSIONS

Read through the three stages of the solution above and think about whether you agree with the conclusions.

● COMMENTS

The weakness of the investigation described above is in its conclusion, which makes a claim about the whole postal service on the basis of just two small samples, which may have contained letters which were highly untypical. (It is possible, for example, that all the first class letters were local, while the second class letters were sent to destinations hundreds of miles away.) Basically, however, the larger the sample you take, the more likely it is to give a fair picture of the overall population. There are statistical methods for testing to see how confident you can be that the differences between the two samples are a true reflection of the two populations from which they were selected. These are called *tests of significance* but the detail of how they are applied is beyond the scope of this book.

Another key area of Statistics involves looking at the relationship between things — 'is smoking linked to cancer?', 'is driving performance linked to alcohol intake?', and so on. The important question here is the *correlation* (or *strength of the relationship*) of the two things under consideration. A strong relationship between two things allows us to be able to predict with some accuracy the value of one of them from the corresponding value of the other. For example, we know that there is quite a close connection between how much alcohol a person drinks and how fast (or slow) their reactions are. If you were told a stranger's alcohol intake you could therefore make quite a good guess at the speed of their reactions. But, to look at another example, taken over a period of years, there seems to be a strong relationship between teachers' salaries and the crime rate. Knowing one of these, one could make a reasonably accurate prediction of the other. Ultimately, of course, we would like to know with more certainty whether the relationship is one of *cause and effect*, but this is trickier to prove. It is one of the classic fallacies in Statistics to assume that a close correlation between two things proves that one causes the other. You will have plenty of opportunities in Chapter 7 to free yourself from this particular fallacy!

WHAT ARE THE MAIN STAGES OF A STATISTICAL INVESTIGATION?

The words in italic in the previous section represent some of the most important concepts in Statistics. Don't worry if you haven't fully understood them yet — you will do by the time you have reached the end of this book. There are, however, other important statistical ideas besides these concepts. These are the statistical approaches to solving problems; the stages that we normally go through when tackling a statistical investigation. Unfortunately many traditional Statistics courses tend to focus only on the data handling side of statistical ideas. But there are other important questions in Statistics — where did the data come from, and why were they collected in the first place?

These questions are central to the way this book has been written. You can't start a statistical investigation without posing a question. For example, the postal investigation in Activity 3 started with the question 'Is the first class post faster than the second class post?'. Thinking about how you might answer this question will help you to decide what data you will need to collect. (In this case the delivery times of a sample of first and second class letters.) The data can then be analysed. I suggest largely graphical methods here, though the postal investigation data were analysed by calculating averages. Finally, there needs to be some conclusion — have you answered your original question? There seem to be four obvious stages to go through and they are described in this book as follows:

The main stages of a statistical investigation

P — Pose the question.   (What do I want to find out?)
C — Collect the data.   (What data will I need?)
A — Analyse the data.   (What do the data show?)
I — Interpret the results.   (Have I answered my question?)

---

 4 USING PCAI

It should help you to sort out your understanding of these four stages if you try to relate them to a particular investigation. Think back to the beer barrels example and try to pick out the four PCAI stages of thinking that the statistician probably went through.

● **COMMENTS**

The likely stages are summarised below:

P — Are the barrels of the right size?
C — Collect the measurements taken from a sample of barrels.
A — Graph the data.
I — Does the graph look sensible? If not, why not?

Together with the concepts given in the previous section, these four stages, summarised as PCAI, form the central ideas in this book and they will structure much of the work contained in the statistical activities that lie ahead.

WHY DO PEOPLE FIND STATISTICS HARD?

It seems there are two main reasons that most students fail to enjoy Statistics and find it hard. The first is that the techniques which they have to master early on are too difficult and these get in the way of the basic concepts. For example, many students find themselves being asked to calculate a coefficient of correlation without really understanding what correlation is all about. The second obstacle that students may face is that usually their statistical work lacks any purpose. Textbook exercises too often involve asking you to do a calculation or draw a graph from a given set of data, with no indication of why this might be a worthwhile thing to do.

In this book these two problems are tackled head on. Firstly, you will be using fairly simple graphical techniques only. The more complicated formulae and statistical tests are not dealt with here and, if you feel you might need them, you will have to consult a more advanced textbook. Secondly, most of the activities will ask you to tackle the complete cycle of statistical work, starting by posing the original problem and seeing it through to some sort of conclusion. Thus, although each chapter deals with particular concepts, these will be 'revealed' to you in the course of doing a variety of everyday statistical investigations.

The next chapter will explain some of the basic terms and ideas about data and measurement. In Chapters 3 and 4 the most useful graphs will be explained and statistical investigating will begin for real in Chapter 5.

SUMMARY

I hope that this introductory chapter has given you some sort of intuitive grasp of what Statistics is all about. Don't worry if you didn't follow all of the explanations of the statistical terms — they will be covered more fully elsewhere in the text. A key feature of the approach taken in the later chapters is to encourage you to tackle the full cycle of statistical thinking. This goes beyond merely 'handling data' to include all four of the PCAI stages (Pose the question, Collect the data, Analyse the data and Interpret the results).

FOLLOW-UP EXERCISES

1   Make a list of all the graphs and diagrams that you are familiar with. Think about the sort of data that they might be used to represent. What sort of conclusions might these graphs help you to come to?

2   Look through the first section of the chapter again and make a note of three justifications for learning Statistics.

3   If you bought two bags of crisps which looked identical, would you expect them to be exactly the same weight? If not, why not?

4   What are the four main stages of a statistical investigation? The following four statements correspond to these four stages but they are in the wrong order. Re-order them correctly.
    (a) I will represent these two sets of data graphically.
    (b) If I compare the two graphs, can I reach a conclusion?
    (c) I will find the heights of a sample of tennis players and also the heights of a sample from the overall population.
    (d) I wonder if tennis players are generally taller than the rest of us?

2 *Digging for Data*

This chapter deals with statistical data — that is the basic facts and figures that are around us.

Key terms: *data, secondary and primary sources, continuous and discrete variables, categories.*

START WITH A CLEAR QUESTION

Have a look at these two titles of possible statistical investigations:

(a) Some aspects of children's TV viewing — a statistical analysis.
(b) Is there a link between children's TV viewing and violence?

Think for a few moments about what might be the basic difference in approach between the two.

Although both these investigations relate to the same general area, there is a big difference in focus. The first one gives no indication of the particular question or questions which the investigator wishes to explore. A report with title (a) above may simply contain tables of data with no clear reason why some data and not others have been included. Since no *question* has been asked, there will be no need for making any conclusions. Anyone who reads such a report might ask, 'So what?'.

The second title, on the other hand, suggests a much more directed investigation. The exercise below asks you to think about what this means in practice.

1 JUDGING A REPORT BY ITS TITLE

What issues would you expect to be discussed in a report with the title given in (b) above? Note them down in the order that you would expect them to be written.

● COMMENTS

In Chapter 1 you read about a simple four stage approach to
carrying out a statistical investigation, denoted by the letters
PCAI. If you can't remember what these letters stand for, look
back to page 8 now and re-read the relevant paragraph. It's a
fair bet that these four stages will form the basic structure of any
statistical report. I've included my comments under these four
headings. Read them through and compare them with what you
have written.

Stage	What you might expect to be covered
Stage P (Pose the question.)	A discussion of what exactly the words 'children's TV viewing' and 'violence' might mean. (For example is it quantity or quality of TV viewing that is being measured, and if it is quality, how do you measure that?)
Stage C (Collect the data.)	How were the data collected? The researcher may have used national or international data or perhaps drawn up his or her own sample (this raises questions of accuracy and reliability).
Stage A (Analyse the data.)	Some formal statistical measures and calculations will be included to show the extent to which the two variables (TV viewing and violence) are linked.
Stage I (Interpret the results.)	What conclusions can be drawn? What other quite different interpretation could fit the facts?

You might be reaching the conclusion that this particular
investigation isn't as straightforward as it first appeared to be.
You are right — it is a can of worms!

However these are the four stages which will be used in this
book. As you tackle each of the investigations which lie ahead,
your first key question will be, 'What exactly is my question?'
You may have to change the wording of your question as you
proceed with the investigation — it will depend partly on what
you want to find out and on what you are able to find out. Here are
a few pointers which should help you to refine and clarify the
purpose of an investigation.

Checklist to help clarify the investigation:

   (i)   What are you trying to find out?
  (ii) What will you need to measure?
 (iii) What units of measure will you use?
 (iv) How will you get your data?
  (v) What sort of data will you get?
 (vi) What will you do with the data?
 (vii) What problems, if any, do you foresee?
(viii) Is your question answerable?
 (ix) What will you do with your results?

The next exercise will give you the opportunity to think a bit more about this checklist of questions.

② PLANNING AN INVESTIGATION

Imagine that you decided to investigate whether there is a link between children's TV viewing and violence. Think for a few minutes how you might set about this and then write down your answers to the nine questions listed above.

● COMMENTS

No doubt this exercise has only confirmed what you already knew; that questions like these are extremely difficult to answer. There are enormous problems of definition, measurement and interpretation. If you are to make a start on exploring statistical ideas using an investigative approach, therefore, I suggest that we look at some simpler and more unambiguous areas of investigation.

③ POSING A CLEAR QUESTION

Listed below are some possible areas of investigation. Each of the three statements is rather vague. Using the checklist above and your common sense, rewrite each statement more precisely into a question which you think you could tackle.

  (a) I wonder how accurate the radar guns are that the police use in 'speed traps'.
  (b) There seem to be too many people in prison.
  (c) The group most at risk are the 'YAMS' (young, accident-prone, male and stupid).

● **COMMENTS**

(a) Perhaps a more clearly worded question might be, 'How do the police decide, on the basis of the car speed data which they collect, whether a motorist really was exceeding the speed limit?'.

(b) The question of whether there are too many people in prison immediately raises the issue of too many compared with what? Are we interested in making historical comparisons over time, or are we concerned with international comparisons based on current data? Alternatively, we might be interested in the question of prison overcrowding — are there too many people in prison compared to the accommodation available? Which ever of these you choose, you will need to be careful when making such comparisons to compare like with like. For example, have a look at these data in figure 2.1.

Year	Prison population
1961	32 600
1987	56 400

Source: Central Statistical Office, *Social Trends 19*, HMSO, London, 1989, p. 193

Figure 2.1   Average prison population in the UK

You can calculate the percentage increase in the prison population over this 26 year period. If you are not sure how this calculation is done, see below:

Actual increase $= 56\,400 - 32\,600$
$= 23\,800$

Percentage increase $= \dfrac{23\,800 \times 100}{32\,600}$
$= 73\%$

So, between 1961 and 1987 there was a 73% increase in the prison population. However, you must remember that the overall population has also risen in this period. A fairer comparison would be between the *proportion* of the population in prison in 1961 and 1987, and these data are shown in figure 2.2.

Year	Average prison population	Total population of UK (million)	Number of prisoners (per one million population)
1961	32 600	52.8	617
1987	56 400	56.9	991

Figure 2.2   Proportion of the population in prison

④ CALCULATING PERCENTAGES

Comparing the figures in the final column of the table above, calculate the percentage increase in the proportion of prisoners per one million population between 1961 and 1987.

● COMMENTS

You should have found that the number of prisoners per one million of population increased by about 61%. This is not quite as large as the earlier calculation suggested. Spend a few minutes now checking that you understand where all the figures in the table came from, exactly how the final percentage was calculated and what this percentage figure actually means.

(c) To check whether the group most at risk is the YAMS we might again turn to the Social Trends publication. However, you need to be clear what is meant by 'at risk'. This term could refer to a wide variety of things; for example, at risk from drug abuse, accidents, disease, moral corruption, ...

Your statistical investigation needs to state clearly which danger or dangers the 'at risk' refers to. Also it is not clear exactly what we mean by 'young'. Usually the word 'young' is used to describe babies and children but in this case it is possible that the term YAMS refers to young men in the 16–24 age range.

Clearly there are many sources of ambiguity in these investigations. However, as is often the case with statistical investigations, we fall back on the key question of '*who wants to know and why?*'. Because question (c) in Activity 3 was really only a textbook exercise, we cannot answer these questions. However, I hope that, during the course of studying this book, you will feel inspired to tackle questions which really concern you. Only when you have posed an interesting question for which you want to find an answer will you be in a position to make these difficult judgements on which data are appropriate to help you reach a conclusion.

SOURCES OF DATA

● PRIMARY AND SECONDARY SOURCES

For a statistical investigation to be really statistical it must involve *data*. A *datum* is a number or figure. Data (the plural of datum) might come from a book, research report, magazine or newspaper. If so, it is said to be taken from a *secondary source*. If, however, you collect the data yourself — perhaps from your own survey or experiment, you are using a *primary source*. On page 131 you will find a brief guide to some of the well-known secondary sources which provide useful data on a variety of issues. Your library should contain most of these but a bit of confidence and practice is needed to track down the source book you require and find appropriate data relevant to your investigation. The exercise below will give you an opportunity to rehearse some of the thinking required in advance.

⑤ CHECKING OUT SECONDARY SOURCES

Using the list of possible sources on page 131, pick out which ones might be relevant to the three statistical investigations that you wrote down in Activity 3.

● COMMENTS

(a) There are no official secondary sources on this question that I am aware of, so for this investigation you might have to consult your local police station. However, they may be a little wary of giving too much away about how they operate in this area! For example, it is likely that they would have to build in some margin of error for the speed shown on the radar gun, and so will be unlikely to prosecute anyone who is shown to have exceeded the limit by, say, only five miles per hour. But for the police to reveal that their margin of error is, say, ten miles per hour might encourage motorists to set out deliberately to exceed the limit by this margin!

(b) *and (c)* The HMSO publication *Social Trends* is an excellent
source of interesting data and would be helpful for both of
these investigations.

CATEGORIES AND VARIABLES

Once the central question of the investigation has been clearly
stated, you should know *what* things you intend to measure (if
you take another look at the checklist on page 13, this is given as
point (ii)). The factors that you will need to measure will be
called either *categories* or *variables*, and we will look at each in
turn.

Categories are fairly straightforward — examples include, eye
colour (blue, brown, etc.), type of vehicle (car, lorry, bus, etc.)
or blood group (A, B, AB, O). Categories are often presented as
boxes to be ticked in a survey. For example, the interviewer may
ask each *respondent* (that means the person taking part in the
survey) to choose from a selection of categories. Here are a few
examples:

Which political party would you vote for?
    Conservative   ☐
    Democrat   ☐
    Green   ☐
    Labour   ☐
    Other   ☐

What type of house do you live in?
    Detached   ☐
    Flat   ☐
    Semi-detached   ☐
    Terrace   ☐
    Other   ☐

Figure 2.3   *Category data in a questionnaire*

Whereas categories are labelled with names, variables are
measured by numbers. Variables are so called because they can
vary, i.e. they can take different values. For example age and
family size are variables because age varies from one person to
another just as family size varies from one family to another.
However, when we come to measure these two variables, there
emerges an important difference between them. See if you can
think what it is.

6 HOW VARIABLES CAN VARY

(a) What is the basic difference between the variables age and family size?

(b) Make a note of two other variables which show this difference.

● **COMMENTS**

You may have noticed that it is impossible to measure someone's age with perfect accuracy — you might know it to the nearest minute, perhaps, but what about the seconds, tenths of seconds, thousandths of a second . . .? With family size, on the other hand, perfect accuracy is possible, because there is a basic unit — people — and they tend to come in whole numbers!

Thus I can tell you that there are *exactly* five people in my family, but the best I can say about my age is that I am *about* 21 years old. Whether or not these two statements are true is quite another matter! All variables, like age, which can be subdivided into infinitely small units are often called *continuous variables*. The other type of variable, of which family size is an example, comes in discrete chunks, and is called a *discrete variable*. The next exercise will give you a chance to think about these two terms and get the important distinction between them clear in your mind.

7 DISCRETE OR CONTINUOUS?

(a) The table below lists a number of variables. Tick each one according to whether you think it is discrete or continuous.

Variable	Discrete	Continuous
(i) The number of milk bottles people buy		
(ii) Feet measurements		
(iii) Shoe sizes		
(iv) The scores when dice are tossed		
(v) Body temperature		

(b) (i) How many possible weekly earnings can there be between £200 and £201?

    (ii) How many possible temperatures can there be between 200°C and 201°C?

● COMMENTS

  (a) Milk bottles, shoe sizes and dice scores come in discrete units (you can't buy 2.37 bottles of milk) and are therefore discrete variables.

    Temperature and feet measurements, on the other hand, can be measured to any degree of accuracy and are not limited by a basic unit, so are examples of continuous variables.

  (b) There are 99 possible earnings between £200 and £201 (these are £200.01, £200.02, . . . £200.99).

    However, there is an infinite number of possible temperatures between 200°C and 201°C (for example, 200.4, 200.417, 200.4170923, and so on).

    The reason for this difference is that earnings is a discrete variable while temperature is continuous.

The two types of variables — continuous and discrete — both describe situations which involve some sort of *scale of measure*. For example, suppose you are carrying out a survey on the number of milk bottles that people buy daily, then each individual family's result could be plotted on a number scale as follows:

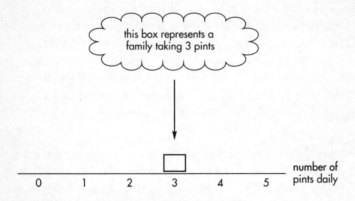

Figure 2.4   *Plotting a number scale*

And if one family can be represented in this way, then all the families sampled can be as well, resulting in a block graph of the whole sample. The results for, say, 20 families might look something like the following:

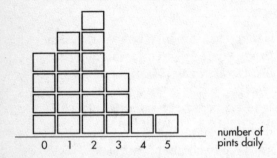

Figure 2.5   Block graph showing the daily milk consumption of 20 families

This block graph reveals patterns in the data which were just not obvious beforehand. Think for a few minutes about some of the common-sense things which you can now say just by glancing at the block graph. These questions will be looked at more closely in Chapter 3.

In one important respect, category data are similar to data derived from discrete variables. What they share is their *discreteness*. The obvious thing to do with category data is to count how many times each category was recorded. If you wish to represent these sort of data graphically, then a barchart or piechart is usually appropriate. So for the remainder of this book the term *discrete* will be used to cover either category data or discrete data from a variable. This is an important point and is summarised in figure 2.6. Spend a few minutes now making sure you understand it.

The important distinction that you will have to remember is the one on the right-hand side of the figure below — that is, between discrete and continuous data. In general, barcharts and piecharts are useful for representing discrete data and you will get a chance to explore these two types of graph in Chapter 3. The sort of graphs that are useful for continuous variables — stemplots, histograms and scatterplots — are covered in Chapter 4. This way of classifying graphs cannot be rigidly applied but is a useful rule of thumb.

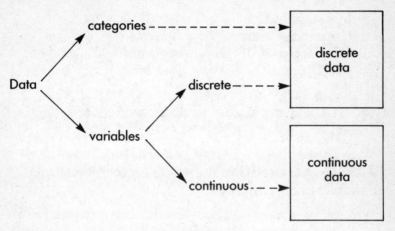

Figure 2.6   A summary of different types of data

SUMMARY

This chapter has looked at the key building block of Statistics which is known as *data* (facts and figures to you and me). The first main distinction which was made was that between categories and variables. The second distinguished the two main types of variables — discrete and continuous. Finally I suggested that the most useful way of thinking about types of data was to classify them into either discrete or continuous.

FOLLOW-UP EXERCISES

1   Pose a clear question to investigate some aspect of house prices. Go through the checklist of nine questions given in the first section of this chapter and answer each question in relation to the investigation you have chosen.

2   What is the difference between a *primary* and a *secondary* source of statistical data?

Below four different sources of data are given. Indicate which is a primary and which is a secondary source.
(a) Asking 30 people in the street for their voting intentions.
(b) Counting how many leaves fall off a shrub each day in Autumn.
(c) Investigating national voting trends based on general election results over the last 40 years.
(d) Keeping a record of the number of times you receive a telephone call that is a wrong number.

3 What is the difference between a *category* and a *variable*? Give an example of each (other than examples used in the chapter).

4 What is the difference between a *discrete variable* and a *continuous variable*. Give an example of each (other than examples used in the chapter).

5 What do *categories* and *discrete variables* have in common?

3 Some Basic Graphs

Key terms: *raw data, vertical and horizontal, bar chart, frequency, tally (chart), histogram, pie chart.*

If your statistical investigation requires you to carry out a survey or experiment, then you will be involved in the collection of primary data. Normally the data will come to you unsorted and will reveal no particular patterns. These are what are known as *raw data*. The skill of the statistician lies in finding ways of reorganising or re-presenting the raw data so that they tell us more about what is being investigated.

The aim of Chapters 3 and 4 is to describe several common ways of reorganising data using graphs. Chapter 5 will show what these graphs can reveal which may not have been obvious from the raw data alone.

This chapter looks at two common ways of representing discrete data — the bar chart and pie chart. Chapter 4 introduces the histogram, stemplot and scatterplot which are normally used with continuous data. If you aren't sure of the distinction between discrete and continuous, look back to page 18 before reading on.

BAR CHART

I usually buy my father socks for Christmas but recently I have noticed that he hasn't tended to wear the ones I have bought him. The family grapevine eventually revealed that my taste in socks is rather 'louder' than my father's. This year I decided to do a little research before plunging in with my luminous green purchase.

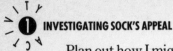

INVESTIGATING SOCK'S APPEAL

Plan out how I might research this item of shopping. Give some thought to each of the four PCAI stages described in the last chapter (they were: Pose the question, Collect the data, Analyse the data, and Interpret the results).

● **COMMENTS**

My own response, based on the four PCAI stages, was as follows:

P— My father clearly wanted his socks to be in tune with other men of his age. I needed to survey *what socks such men were wearing*.

C— The next time I was queuing in a railway station I *jotted down a description of the sockware* of 20 smartly dressed gentlemen, see below:

---

red, black, green, maroon, blue, patterned, blue, patterned, black, grey, grey, blue, green, black, blue, maroon, patterned, brown, blue, black.

A— On its own, this list of raw data wasn't very helpful. Figures 3.1, 3.2 and 3.3 are three different ways of reorganising the data to reveal the patterns.

All three representations share the common feature that the socks are grouped into useful categories—their colours. It is thereby easier to count how many socks are in each category.

I— I decided to play safe and this year again, my father got two socks; one blue and the other black! (And I have another pair just like it for his birthday!)

			blue		
	black		blue		
	black		blue	patterned	
	black	green	maroon	blue	patterned	grey
red	black	green	maroon	blue	patterned	grey

Figure 3.1   Sock colours

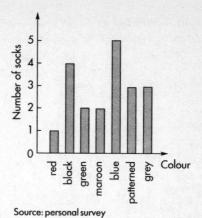

Colour	Number
red	1
black	4
green	2
maroon	2
blue	5
patterned	3
grey	2

Source: personal survey

Source: personal survey

Figure 3.2   Table showing sock colours

Figure 3.3   Bar chart showing sock colours

The third representation shown, the *bar chart*, is one of the most common of all graphs. However, it doesn't provide much more information than the table. The main advantage of the bar chart is that it allows you to see at a glance which columns have the greatest values (the tallest bars) and which have the least value (the smallest bars).

The next exercise asks you to think about how a bar chart is drawn and how it should or should not be interpreted. The six questions listed raise some of the key issues concerning the meaning of a bar chart. Jot down your own answers to them and then compare what you have written with the comments below.

② UNDERSTANDING A BAR CHART

Answer the following questions about the bar chart in figure 3.4:

(a) What does the vertical scale (i.e. the one going up the left-hand side of the graph) tell you?

(b) What sort of data are suitable for being drawn on a bar chart?

(c) Why do you think the bars have been drawn so that there are gaps between them?

(d) Would it matter if the bars did not all have the same width?

(e) Are the bars in this bar chart placed in any particular order along the horizontal scale (i.e. the line going along the bottom)? Is there a more useful way of ordering the bars?

(f) Might there have been a quicker way of recording and graphing these data?

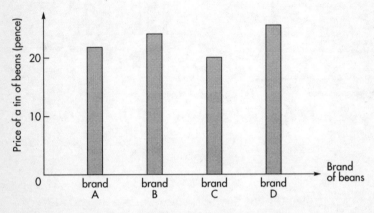

Source: personal survey

Figure 3.4   Bar chart showing prices of beans

● COMMENTS

(a) In figure 3.3, the vertical scale gives a count of the number of items in each group. This is sometimes known as the *frequency*. This is not always true of bar charts, as the baked beans example shows.

(b) The bar chart should be used only with discrete data. If you want to represent continuous data in this way, a slightly different form of block graph, called a histogram, is needed (see page 35).

(c) The gaps between the bars are there to stress the fact that these categories are quite separate (i.e. discrete).

(d) The bars should all have the same width because otherwise you might give a false impression of the importance of some of the categories. The equal width of the bars stresses the fact that each category is equally important. Any differences in frequency will be recorded by differences in the heights of the bars, not by their widths.

(e) I have not given any special ordering to the bars, other than simply the order in which I first recorded each price. However, since these four prices do not offer any obvious 'natural' order, it might have been more helpful to redraw the bar chart with the bars in increasing order of price, thus:

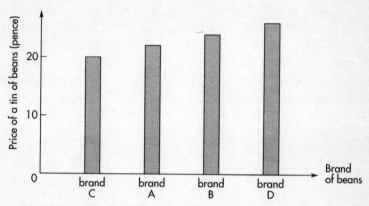

Source: personal survey

Figure 3.5   Figure 3.4 redrawn with bars in order of frequency

Note, however, that sometimes there *is* a natural ordering on the horizontal scale which must be preserved. An example of this is shown below with the following data:

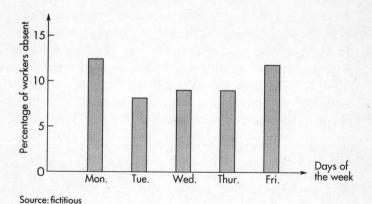

Source: fictitious

Figure 3.6   Percentage of workers absent from work over a typical week

(f) There is a quicker way of recording this sort of data which allows you to draw the chart almost directly as the raw data are gathered. It is called making a *tally* or drawing a *tally chart*. If at all possible, you should write down beforehand which categories you expect to come up in your survey. Then when you carry out the survey, simply tick each category every time it appears. Of course, it isn't always possible to predict each category in advance of carrying out the survey, so you may have to leave room for new categories as they appear. If you are doing a large survey, it may be time-consuming to count all the ticks in each category at the end. A simpler approach is to tally in fives or record directly onto squared paper. An example of each is shown below:

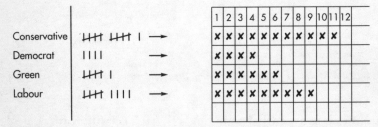

Source: fictitious

Figure 3.7　Tallying in fives　　*Figure 3.8　A tally chart using squared paper*

As a final piece of advice about drawing a bar chart, it is worth clearly stating the title and labelling the horizontal and vertical scales. The source of the data should also be given at the bottom of the graph. Without all this information it is often quite hard to understand what the graph is about or how you might set about finding out further information about it.

To end this section on the bar chart, have a go at Activity 3, which will revise most of the points covered so far.

③　A FAULTY BAR CHART

The bar chart in figure 3.9 contains several deliberate mistakes. See how many you can spot and then quickly sketch your own improved version. When you have done that, compare your bar chart with my improved version in the summary at the end of the chapter.

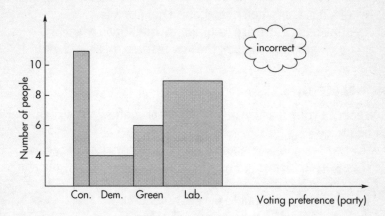

Figure 3.9   Faulty bar chart showing voting preferences

PIE CHART

The 'socks' data from the previous section could have been drawn as a pie chart rather than a bar chart. Thus:

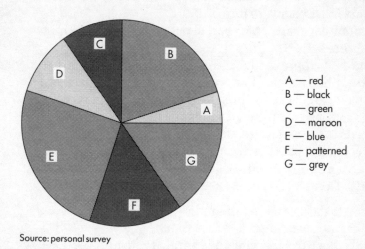

A — red
B — black
C — green
D — maroon
E — blue
F — patterned
G — grey

Source: personal survey

Figure 3.10   Pie chart showing the data from the socks survey

The size of each 'slice' of the pie is a measure of the number of items in each category. I won't explain here the exact details of how to draw each slice to the appropriate size. It is more important to understand what a pie chart shows and to recognise the sort of situations when it might be a helpful way of representing data. Here are a number of questions which will draw your attention to some of the key features of a pie chart.

④ UNDERSTANDING A PIE CHART

(a) What can you measure on the pie chart to show the size of each 'slice'?

(b) What sort of data are suitable for being drawn on a pie chart?

(c) When you are drawing a pie chart, does it matter how big you draw the circle representing the pie?

(d) How many slices should a pie chart contain?

(e) Draw the 'baked bean' data as a pie chart (a quick sketch will do). Which is more helpful for these data, a bar chart or a pie chart?

● COMMENTS

(a) The angle that each slice makes at the centre of the pie is the best way of measuring its size. If, for example, a particular slice makes a 90° angle at the centre of the pie, this indicates that it contains one quarter of the total items (90° is one quarter of a complete turn of 360°).

(b) As for a bar chart, a pie chart should only be used with discrete data.

(c) The circle representing the complete pie can be drawn to any size within reason. However, if you wish to compare two similar pie charts side by side, the size of each pie is usually taken to indicate the *total* number of items in each pie. Care needs to be taken here, because it is the *areas* of each pie which will enable this comparison to be made and you will therefore be involved in calculations using the formula for the area of a circle. A typical example is shown in figure 3.11.

Note that there were rather more than 1½ times as many males as females enrolled as part-time students in 1986/7 so the first pie has therefore been drawn with a proportionately larger area than the second.

Males (222.8 thousand)

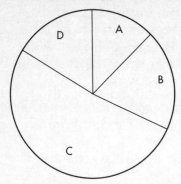

Females (136.1 thousand)

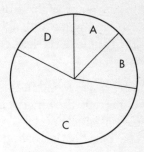

Key:

A Universities
B Open University
C Polytechnics and colleges — part-time day courses
D Polytechnics and colleges — evening only courses

Source: Central Statistical Office, *Social Trends 19*, London, HMSO, 1989, p. 60

Figure 3.11   Part-time students in higher education, 1986/7

(d) There is no particular number of slices which a pie chart
should contain as this will largely depend on the number of
categories in the raw data. However, if there are too few —
say only two — it will look rather silly and if there are too
many (say 10 or more), it is hard to see any overall pattern.

A — black
B — blue
C — patterned
D — other

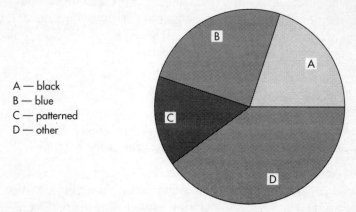

Figure 3.12   Redrawn socks pie chart

One solution to having too many categories is to group some of them together into a different wider category, or perhaps collapse some of the smaller categories into a general 'other' heading. Figure 3.12 shows how the 'socks' pie chart would look if some of the less popular colours were collapsed in this way.

Note, however, that this 'other' category is not very useful, for it is only the biggest category because it is made up of several small ones.

(e) A pie chart of the 'baked bean' data would look something like this:

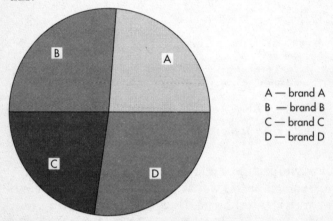

A — brand A
B — brand B
C — brand C
D — brand D

Figure 3.13   Prices of baked beans

This is actually a fairly meaningless representation. Think for a moment about what the complete pie represents here. It is simply the sum of various baked bean prices, which is really of no importance at all. The point to be learned from this is that if you wish to choose a pie chart to represent your data, the complete pie (representing the total of all the categories) should have some useful meaning.

Finally, as with all graphs, don't forget to include title and labels where appropriate and add the data source at the bottom.

The bar chart and pie chart are useful ways of graphing discrete data. If you have collected continuous data, however, a better choice would be a histogram or a stemplot. These are described in the following chapter.

SUMMARY

This chapter looked at two useful graphs for representing discrete data — the bar chart and the pie chart. Bar charts indicate the frequency by the height of each bar, whereas pie charts indicate frequency by the angle at the centre of each slice.

Finally, figure 3.14 below shows the improved version of the incorrectly drawn bar chart in figure 3.9.

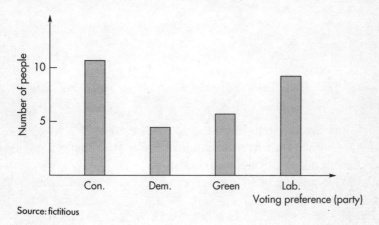

Source: fictitious

Figure 3.14   Improved bar chart showing voting preferences

FOLLOW-UP EXERCISES

1   Which of the following types of data are bar charts and pie charts particularly suitable for portraying.
Data taken from:
     (a) a discrete variable
     (b) a category
     (c) a continuous variable?

2   Why are bar charts normally drawn with gaps between the bars?

3   The pie chart in figure 3.15 overleaf shows the proportions of the various gases in the atmosphere that contribute to the greenhouse effect. Estimate the percentage of each gas.

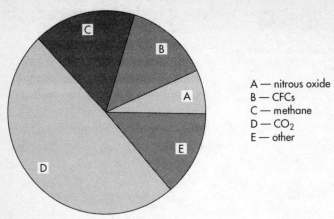

A — nitrous oxide
B — CFCs
C — methane
D — CO_2
E — other

Source: *Radio Times*, 3rd–9th June, 1989, p. 5

Figure 3.15   Breakdown of gases contributing to the greenhouse effect

4 The bar chart below shows the share of all radio listening by radio station taken from a sample of adults who have access to Independent Local Radio (ILR).

    (a) What are the main features revealed here about radio listening in Britain?

    (b) How can Radio 1 DJs substantiate their claim that Radio 1 is 'the most listened to radio station in Britain'?

    (c) Re-present the same data using two pie charts.

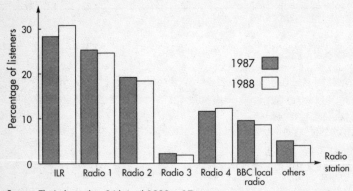

Source: *The Independent*, 26th April, 1989, p. 17

Figure 3.16   The share of all listening by radio station

5 Suppose you wished to find a way of representing the ages of five people graphically. Which type of graph (a bar chart or a pie chart) would be most suitable and why?

4 *Some More Basic Graphs*

This chapter covers three extremely useful graphs which are commonly used to represent continuous data.

Key terms: *histogram, average, mode, mean, median, stemplot, scatterplot.*

HISTOGRAM

How heavy is an egg? Clearly it all depends on the egg, as they come in different sizes. But why do eggs vary at all? Well, it seems that the age of the hen is one critical factor. Hens enter the world of egg production offering rather small eggs and these gradually increase to a peak. After the hen is 'over the hill', reproductively speaking, and its eggs start to become smaller, the bird is usually 'invited' to vacate its cage and make way for a younger hen. No, it's not much fun being a battery hen. But, to return to the question which started this section, let's look more closely at the weight of eggs.

 1 INVESTIGATING EGGS

Think about how you would carry out a statistical investigation about the weight of eggs. Jot down a few notes describing what you would do using the four PCAI headings which structured your answer to Activity 1 of Chapter 3.

● **COMMENTS**

My own response, based on the four PCAI stages, is as follows:

P—A more clearly worded question is 'what does a typical egg weigh?'

C—Finding the relevant data involves weighing a number of eggs. Clearly it is not sufficient to buy a box of eggs that you would find in the supermarket and start weighing them.

Since the eggs have already been graded for size, the sample of eggs in a particular box will all weigh roughly the same. You need to move further back in the egg production line and weigh a few eggs at source. The table below lists the weights, measured to the nearest tenth of a gram, of 30 eggs chosen at random before they rolled towards the egg-grading machine.

64.1, 53.8, 67.2, 60.0, 50.7, 73.3, 60.2, 56.9, 58.6, 66.3,
56.0, 48.2, 58.7, 67.2, 68.0, 68.4, 51.6, 74.3, 62.8, 64.4,
60.9, 73.2, 63.5, 71.2, 65.3, 54.8, 67.9, 62.6, 56.4, 61.2.

Source: based on Government Statistical Service, *Ministry of Agriculture, Fisheries and Food Statistics,*
Issue no. 3/88, 24th January, 1988, p. 1.

Figure 4.1   Weight of 30 eggs measured to the nearest 0.1 g

A—The most sensible way of analysing these data is to sort the numbers into groups. Intervals of five grams seem suitable and here is how they would look as a tally chart.

Weight (g)	Tally
45 – 50	
50 – 55	1
55 – 60	
60 – 65	1
65 – 70	
70 – 75	

Figure 4.2   Tally chart showing the weights of 30 eggs

I've done the first two for you. The egg weighing 64.1 g falls into the 60–65 g category so a tally is marked against that group. Similarly, the egg weighing 53.8 g shows up against the 50–55 g group. You might like to complete tally chart for yourself. However, before you do, there is one problem which needs to be sorted out. That is how to decide where to record weights which fall onto the boundaries of the groups. For example, the fourth weight recorded is 60.0 g. Clearly this lies *both* in the 55–60 g range and the 60–65 g range. One possible solution might be to define the limits of the lower range as 55–59 g and then the next range will become 60–64 g, and so on. Clearly this avoids the problem of overlapping values at the boundary but creates a new difficulty of introducing 'holes' at each boundary. (Where, for example, should an egg weighing 59.5 g be placed?)

We therefore need to define the boundaries of the groups so that they neither overlap nor leave holes. There are several ways of doing this, most of which are unnecessarily complicated. The system which I favour is to write the group 'from 55 up to but not including 60' as:

55–⁻60

Note the 'minus' sign above and just to the left of the 60, which tells you that 60 is *not* included in this group but any value just less than 60 g is. The next group will therefore be 60–⁻65 and will include every value from 60 up to but not including 65 g.

Here is how the egg weights would look if they were represented as a histogram:

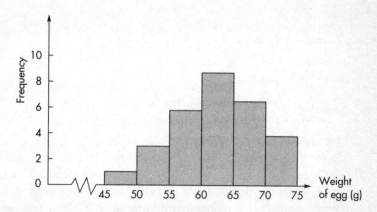

Figure 4.3   Weights of 30 eggs

As you can see, the histogram looks similar to a bar chart. However the key difference is that the bars of a histogram are allowed to touch. Think for a moment as to why this is. The main factor which distinguishes a bar chart from a histogram is that a bar chart is used to portray discrete data while a histogram shows continuous data. So, with a histogram, the horizontal scale describes a continuous variable (in this example, weight) while the vertical scale shows frequency — i.e. the number of items in each group.

I —The final stage in the PCAI cycle is the interpretation of the graph. What does the histogram reveal about the typical weight of an egg? Perhaps the simplest way of answering this is to look for the tallest column in the histogram. This reveals that the most common egg weight is the 60– ⁻65 g range. This is a sort of average of the data and is called the *mode*. The mode is the value (or range of values) which occurs most frequently.

Of course, we might not have chosen to graph the data at all. An alternative would have been to add all 30 weights together and divide by 30. This gives the result of 62.2 g, which is a different sort of average, known as the *mean*. The mean is found by adding all the values together and dividing by the number of values. There is a third common type of average, called the *median*, which will be defined in the next section.

The next exercise raises some important issues about the meaning of a histogram and how it can be interpreted. It should help you to consolidate your grasp of this idea.

② UNDERSTANDING A HISTOGRAM

(a) What does the vertical scale on the histogram tell you?
(b) What sort of data are suitable for being drawn on a histogram?
(c) Why are the columns on a histogram allowed to touch?
(d) Can a histogram be drawn from a tally chart which had unequal intervals? For example, what would happen if two of these groups were collapsed into one so that there were four intervals of 5 g width and one of 10 g?

(e) Can the columns of a histogram be recorded in the same way as the bars of a bar chart?

(f) Is it possible to record data directly onto a histogram?

(g) Why do we bother to draw histograms at all?

● COMMENTS

(a) Although in a bar chart the vertical scale may or may not measure frequency, in a histogram it is *always* a measure of frequency. Provided all the columns are of equal width, you can mark the frequencies on this vertical scale. What happens when the columns differ in width is more complicated and this is discussed under point (d) below.

(b) Whereas the bar chart and pie chart are designed to show discrete data, the histogram is only suitable for continuous data.

(c) Continuous data, like weight, height, time, and so on, are not restricted to a particular number of possible values. Since continuous data can fall on any point on the horizontal number scale, the columns of the histogram must be allowed to touch.

(d) It is possible to draw a histogram from a tally chart with unequal intervals, but in general this practice should be avoided. The problem is that if a particular interval is twice as wide as the others, it will show up twice as many values as if it had been the normal width. The difficulty is solved by *halving* the height of that column. Similarly, if an interval is three times the normal width, then the column height should be shortened to one third, and so on. However, this procedure makes it difficult to interpret the vertical scale. Don't worry if this all seems hard to follow — it is really beyond the scope of this book and I don't propose to offer a detailed explanation here.

(e) Please note that, unlike with most bar charts, you can't interfere with the order of the columns of a histogram. This is for the obvious reason that the columns lie in a natural sequence as described on the horizontal scale and this cannot be rearranged.

(f) Provided you know in advance the sort of range of data you expect to collect, they *can* be recorded directly onto a histogram. After all, this is really little more than completing

39

a tally chart except that each value is recorded as a little rectangle instead of as a tally mark. The other difference is that a tally chart usually records the frequencies horizontally while histograms show them as vertical columns. A word of warning, however: Note that when you record data directly onto either a tally chart or a histogram you lose all trace of the original data. So, if you wished, subsequently, to calculate the mean of the raw data, you could only make an estimate of it. Also, if you find that you have entered a value incorrectly onto the histogram, this will be difficult to correct without the raw data. These are problems which the stemplot overcomes (see section below).

(g) It is one thing to be able to draw a histogram. It is quite another to appreciate when and why this sort of graph might be useful. The simple answer is that the histogram reveals patterns in data that are just not obvious from looking at the raw data alone. It shows up the typical or average values and gives a good indication of how widely spread the data are. These are such important questions that the whole of the next chapter will be devoted to them. They will also form the foundations for most of the rest of this book.

STEMPLOT

The second graph examined in this section is the stemplot. To illustrate the stemplot, we will refer back to the egg weight data on page 36. Like the histogram, it is used with continuous data, though it can sometimes also be used with discrete data. A stemplot is very similar to a tally chart except that the tally marks are replaced by the final digits of the raw data. For example, as you will see from the stemplot below, the number 64 will be recorded on the stemplot by entering the final digit, i.e. the '4', in the appropriate row. This type of graph is sometimes known as a 'stem and leaf' diagram. As you will see from this example, the 'stems' here correspond to the tens digits of the 30 numbers. Attached to these stems are the 'leaves', which correspond to the units digits of the numbers. You will notice that we have not been able to represent the egg weights to three-figure accuracy and the egg weights given in figure 4.1 have had to be rounded to the nearest gram. For example, the weight of the first egg,

64.1 g, is rounded down to 64 g. The second egg, which weighed 53.8 g, is rounded up to 54 g, and so on.

```
7—
6—
6— 4
5—
5—
4—
```

Figure 4.4   Stemplot showing weight, in grams, of one egg weighing 64 g

Here the first egg in the batch, with a weight of 64 g, is recorded on the lower of the two 'sixty' stems and its position is marked using the digit '4'. The next weight, 54 g, will be recorded with a '4' in the same way but opposite the lower of the 'fifty' stems. The complete stemplot will look something like this:

N=30

```
H=74   7—3431
       6—7678858
       6—400341431
       5—796956
       5—412
L=48   4—8
```

Note: 4—8 means 48 g
    N = number of items in the sample
    H = highest value in the sample
    L = lowest value in the sample

Source: figure 4.1

Figure 4.5   Stemplot showing the weights, in grams, of a sample of 30 eggs

As for the histogram, a feature of the stemplot is that the 'shape' and patterns of the data quickly become apparent as the data are recorded. However a unique feature of the stemplot is that the original data are not lost — you see the values appearing as 'leaves' on the display. Provided you have a rough idea beforehand of what range of values to expect, the stems can be prepared in advance and then the data recorded directly onto them. The only untidiness about this stemplot is that the 'leaves' on each stem are out of sequence. These can easily be shuffled, producing an ordered stemplot, as follows:

N=30

H=74	7—1334
	6—5677888
	6—001133444
	5—566799
	5—124
L=48	4—8

Note: 4—8 means 48 g

Figure 4.6   Ordered stemplot showing the weights, in grams, of a sample of 30 eggs

❸ UNDERSTANDING A STEMPLOT

Here are some questions to get you thinking further about the stemplot.

(a) What is the width of each interval in the stemplot above?

(b) Can stemplots be drawn using a pencil and paper only?

(c) In a stemplot, are the stems always the tens and the leaves always the units?

(d) In this example the stems increase as you go up the vertical scale. Can they be drawn the other way round?

(e) Is there *any* loss of data when they are recorded directly onto a stemplot?

(f) What do you do when a value appears which is far away from the range of values covered by the stems? For example, how would you record an ostrich egg weighing in at 145 g on this stemplot?

(g) Can the stemplot show patterns in the data in the same way as the histogram?

● COMMENTS

(a) Since there are two stems for each lot of tens (two for 50, two for 60, . . .) each stem covers an interval of 5 g. Note that this is exactly the same as for the histogram in Section 1. Thus, the lower of the 'fifty' stems contains values in the range 50–54, while the upper 'fifty' stem covers the range 55–59.

(b) Stemplots *can* be drawn using a pencil and paper only, but care needs to be taken to ensure that the leaves are equally spaced. The typewriter takes care of this automatically, but hand-drawn stemplots are best done on squared paper.

(c) It is *not* true that the stems always represent the tens digits of the data and the leaves the units. If, for example, you wished to record numbers like 688 and 742 on a stemplot, you might first round these numbers to the nearest ten (producing 690 and 740). The stems would then become the hundreds digits (6, 7, . . .) and the leaves would be the tens (9, 4, . . .).

(d) In many textbooks stemplots are drawn the other way up. I have chosen this way round because I tend to think of things increasing as they go up (just like the vertical scale on other graphs).

(e) Very little is lost by recording data directly onto a stemplot *except* the order in which the data were collected. Usually this is not important, but sometimes we wish to investigate if there are patterns in the data over time. In these circumstances a stemplot should not be used.

(f) Values which are far removed from the rest are not normally recorded with the others but are shown above or below the horizontal lines as *outliers*. Thus, the mighty ostrich egg would show up as follows:

N=31

Outliers   145

H=74 7—1334
      6—5677888
      etc.

Figure 4.7   Part of a stemplot showing an ostrich egg as an outlier

(g) The stemplot is just as effective as the histogram in showing up patterns in the data — indeed, even more so, since all the original data are preserved. Thus it is possible to identify particular items of data from the stemplot in terms of their order of size. So it is easy to see that, ignoring the extreme outlier of 145 g, the heaviest egg is 74 g, the fourth lightest egg is 54 g, and so on. This seems a good moment to introduce the third of our common averages — the *median*. The median is the value of the middle item when they are ranked in order of size. In this case there are 30 items, so the median can be taken to lie half way between the fifteenth and sixteenth items. You can easily count through the stemplot in sequence starting with the smallest value to find that both the fifteenth and sixteenth values are 63. Thus the median value of these data is 63 g.

SCATTERPLOT

Do people tend to buy more icecreams on a hot day? From previous experience the answer to this question is fairly obviously yes. Let's now ask a similar but rather more subtle question.

'Is it true that, in general, the hotter the day the more icecreams are bought?'

To investigate this statistically, you won't get very far without some data. Have a look now at the table below:

Day	Sales (litres)	Temperature (°C)
Monday	21	18
Tuesday	25	20
Wednesday	15	15
Thursday	24	21
Friday	26	22
Saturday	32	20
Sunday	0	19

Source: fictitious

Figure 4.8   Icecream sales and temperature

The most useful way of representing this sort of information graphically is with a *scatterplot* (sometimes also called *scatter graph* or *scatter diagram*), and this is shown below.

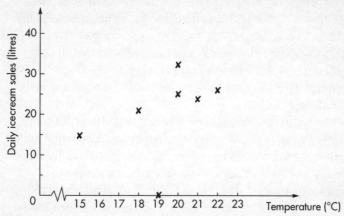

Figure 4.9   Scatterplot showing icecream sales and temperature

The next activity raises some questions about the meaning of a scatterplot and how it can be interpreted.

④ UNDERSTANDING A SCATTERPLOT

(a) Which variable has been recorded on the horizontal axis? Which variable has been recorded on the vertical axis?
(b) Could the scatterplot have been drawn with the axes the other way round?
(c) How would you describe the pattern of points overall?
(d) Which points don't seem to fit the overall pattern? Why do you think they are different from the others?
(e) What conclusions, if any, could another icecream seller draw from this graph about their own sales?

● **COMMENTS**

(a) The variable on the horizontal axis is temperature. The variable on the vertical axis is icecream sales.
(b) With some scatterplots is does not really matter which way round the axes are drawn. However, there is an important convention which, where it applies (as it does here), should be used. This is to pick out which of the two variables is more

likely to be independent of the other one. This independent variable then goes on the horizontal axis. So in this example the temperature will not be affected by icecream sales and has therefore been taken to be the independent variable. (Note that it is theoretically possible for icecream sales on a particular day to be so massive that the air temperature drops as a result. However, you must judge for yourself whether this is a sensible interpretation!)

(c) In general, the shape of the scatterplot is to slope upwards and to the right.

(d) The points corresponding to Saturday and Sunday don't fit the overall pattern. Saturday's sales of icecream were very high despite fairly average temperatures that day. This is probably due to the fact that there are more shoppers available to buy icecreams on a Saturday and also because they are in a more relaxed mood. The zero sales on Sunday may have been due to the fact that the shop was closed that day.

(e) Overall the scatterplot does seem to confirm that there is a link between icecream sales and temperature; in general, more icecream is sold on warmer days, although weekend consumption is rather different from that of weekdays. However, the sample of seven points represented here is very small and, like most 'findings' in Statistics, the link has not been conclusively proved.

SUMMARY

In this chapter you have been introduced to three important graphs used to represent continuous data — the histogram, stemplot and scatterplot, and three measures of average — mean, median and mode. The histogram and stemplot are useful for investigating patterns in a set of values taken from a single variable (for example, the weight of a sample of eggs). Scatterplots are useful for exploring relationships between two variables (for example, the connection between leg length and running speed). In the next chapter you will get an opportunity to use these graphs to help solve problems in a statistical investigation.

FOLLOW-UP EXERCISES

The follow-up exercises are all based on the following data taken from the Wimbledon Tennis Championships, 1989.

Rank	Name	Age	Height (m)	Career earnings (millions of pounds)	Country
1	I. Lendl	29	1.88 (6′ 2″)	8.8	Cz
2	S. Edberg	23	1.88 (6′ 2″)	3.4	Sweden
3	B. Becker	21	1.88 (6′ 2″)	3.1	W Germany
4	M. Wilander	24	1.83 (6′ 0″)	4.4	Sweden
5	J. McEnroe	30	1.80 (5′ 11″)	6.5	US
6	J. Hlasek	24	1.90 (6′ 3″)	0.9	Switz
7	M. Mecir	25	1.83 (6′ 0″)	1.5	Cz
8	T. Mayotte	28	1.90 (6′ 3″)	1.3	US
1	S. Graf	20	1.75 (5′ 9″)	2.4	W Germany
2	M. Navratilova	32	1.73 (5′ 8″)	8.9	US
3	G. Sabatini	19	1.73 (5′ 8″)	1.4	Arg
4	C. Evert	34	1.70 (5′ 7″)	5.5	US
5	Z. Garrison	25	1.65 (5′ 5″)	1.1	US
6	H. Sukova	24	1.88 (6′ 2″)	1.66	Cz
7	A. Sanchez	17	1.67 (5′ 6″)	0.34	Spain
8	P. Shriver	26	1.83 (6′ 0″)	2.6	US

Source: data compiled from various sources

Figure 4.10   The top men and women seeds at Wimbledon, 1989

1   Taking all 16 players together, draw a histogram to represent their career earnings.

2   Draw a back-to-back stemplot comparing the heights of these 8 men and 8 women.

3   Draw a scatterplot between age and earnings of these 16 players.

5 Showing the Spread

This chapter is about the important ideas of variation, distribution and spread.

Variation is a fact of life. It refers to the obvious point that no two things, however similar, are exactly the same; there will always be some variation between them.

Distributions can be thought of as graphs which describe the pattern of variation in a set of numbers.

Spread describes just how much variation there is.

The graph below illustrates these three terms more clearly.

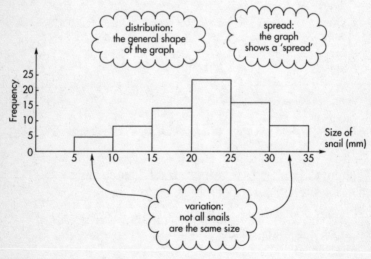

Figure 5.1   Sizes of snails

Key terms: *spread, histogram, stemplot, variation, distribution, variable, continuous and discrete variables, cumulative percentage table, range, central peak, upper and lower tails, (percentage) frequency table.*

DRAWING THE DISTRIBUTION

'We could reach you in 40 minutes flat!', boasts a well-known motoring organisation recovery service advertisement. Sounds impressive, or does it? Well, it really depends on what they mean by 'could'. Does it mean 'most of the time', or 'some of the time', or only in the (unlikely) event of where the breakdown was caused by a collision with the organisation's rescue truck?

The small print of the advertisement is a bit more specific, and, indeed, more encouraging. 'In fact we reach over 80% of breakdowns within an hour', it says.

This second statement reveals rather more about the likelihoods involved. It might be possible to check this statement by taking a sample of, say, 100 breakdown times, and confirming that at least 80 of them were rescued in less than one hour. In fact, even though there are no such data easily available, it is possible to have a rough idea of what the overall shape of these data might look like.

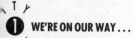 WE'RE ON OUR WAY...

Sketch out a histogram showing what you think a plot of the distribution of 100 breakdown recovery times might look like.

● COMMENTS

We really know only two facts here. One is that *at least some* of the breakdowns were reached in 40 minutes. The second is that 80% of them were reached in one hour. Just how long it took for the other 20% of breakdowns to be reached isn't known. The two histograms shown in figures 5.2 and 5.3 overleaf are made up, but either would be possible according to the information given. They represent, respectively, the 'best' and one of the 'worst' possible patterns of breakdown rescue times.

The reason for starting with this example is to show that, quite often, a single fact can conceal a complex pattern of facts which may lie behind it. In particular, if we are trying to get a better picture of something, taking a single measure of it only provides a snapshot of its value at that particular moment. Measuring it 100 times allows us to gain an insight into how it varies. If we

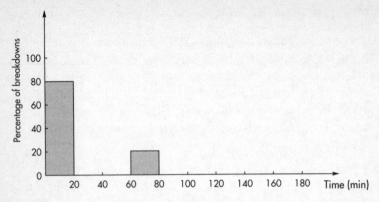

Figure 5.2 '*Best' possible pattern of breakdown rescue times*

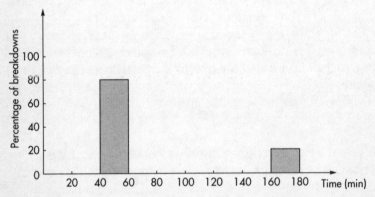

Figure 5.3 '*Worst' possible pattern of breakdown rescue times*

represent these data as a histogram or stemplot we can get a picture of this variation. The shape of this picture is what we call the *distribution* of the data. What this means, literally, is whether there are lots of high values or low values or whether they are mostly bunched in the middle. As you will see throughout the rest of this chapter (and also as indicated in Chapter 1), most distributions tend to be bunched in the middle.

The rest of this chapter will provide different examples of this basic idea of a distribution.

'Is she/he all right?' is invariably the first question a mother will ask on giving birth. What she probably means is, 'Is my baby normal, both physically and mentally?'. We would not want our

children to be abnormally tall or short, or abnormally fat or thin.
Neither do we want them to have an abnormal number of fingers
or heads. However, the way that the word 'normal' is applied to
the number of heads or fingers we have is rather different to how
it may describe our height or weight.

② WHAT'S NORMAL?

(a) Give two examples of a 'normal' height for an adult female.
(b) Give two examples of a 'normal' number of heads for an adult
    female.

● COMMENTS

(a) A woman of, say, 1.55 m (5 ft 1 inch) or 1.73 m (5 ft
    8 inches) would be considered 'normal'.
(b) One head is 'normal' — no more or less! Therefore it is not
    possible to give *two* examples here.

This activity has picked up two important differences between
what we would consider a normal height and a normal number of
heads. The first is that height is a continuous variable. This
means that there are an infinite number of possible heights that a
person can be — it all depends on the degree of accuracy with
which you are prepared to measure them. Number of heads,
however, is a discrete variable — which means that the possible
values available are restricted because they come in 'discrete'
steps (no heads, one head, two heads, . . .). This idea was
explained in Chapter 2 (Activity 7), so you may like to stop
reading now and look back over it again.

The second difference between these two variables lies in how
widely spread the possible values could be, for them to count as
'normal'. Unlike the 'normal number of heads', there is a wide
range of heights a woman could be and still be counted 'normal'.
Just how tall or how short you would have to be to count as
'abnormal' really depends on how widely you cast your definition
of what is 'normal'.

③ 'OOH . . . ISN'T SHE . . . AVERAGE?'

Beatrice's birth weight was 4060 g (8 lb 15 oz). Is this
abnormally heavy? Plan how you might investigate this question

using the PCAI stages described in Chapter 1. To remind you, here they are again:

P — Pose the question.
C — Collect the data.
A — Analyse the data.
I — Interpret the results.

● COMMENTS

Here is one solution to this question:

P— Just how abnormally heavy Beatrice's weight is depends on the answer to the following question: 'How does her birth weight compare with that of other babies?'

C— Birth weight data can be gathered from weight charts provided in post-natal clinics. The table below summarises these:

% Babies	3	10	25	50	75	90	97
Weight (g) less than	2500	2800	3100	3350	3700	3950	4350

Source: J. M. Tanner et al., *Archives of Diseases in Childhood*, Volume 41, 1966

Figure 5.4   Birth weights shown on a weight chart

A— This table is called a *cumulative percentage table* because the percentages 'cumulate' (i.e. they add together) as you go from left to right through the table. What the table means is that 3% of babies weighed less than 2500 g, 10% weighed less than 2800 g, and so on. (Note that these figures have been rounded to the nearest 50 g.) These data are shown plotted on a graph in figure 5.5. This type of graph is called a *cumulative percentage graph*.

If we draw a vertical line at Beatrice's weight (also shown on the graph) we can then get a sense of how typical her weight is.

I— The graph shows that Beatrice's weight is just above the 90% mark. If we estimate this as, say, 92%, this means that something like 8% of babies have a birth weight higher than

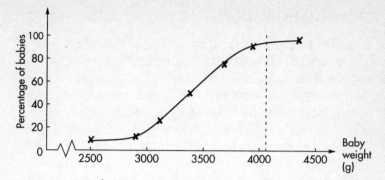

Figure 5.5   Cumulative percentage graph showing birth weights

Beatrice. Now you might now be thinking, 'So what? Does this mean she is or she isn't abnormally heavy?' The answer is that it really is up to *you* to decide where to draw the line. It is just a matter of convention. For most practical situations we often take the *middle* 95% of the range as being 'normal' and anything outside that may be considered abnormal. Clearly, Beatrice's birth weight is well inside this range and, although above average in weight, she is not abnormally heavy, according to the 'middle 95%' definition of normality.

This investigation may have raised several further questions for you about how these data might have been interpreted. For example, the small print on the chart might reveal that the data were based on measurements taken before 1966. With better general standards of nutrition and health, current birth weights may be rather different, so we may not be making a fair comparison. Also, although a full-term baby spends about 40 weeks in the womb, many are born after considerably less or more time. This is another example of variation and it will affect the baby's weight. So, if Beatrice was born at, say, only 36 weeks, it would not be fair to compare her weight alongside the weights of full-term babies.

Another important issue is worth following up in more detail. It is what we mean exactly by the middle 95% or 99% of a distribution and this is explained in the next section.

COMPARING DISTRIBUTIONS

The term MOR (middle of the road) is usually taken to refer to popular music which is neither one extreme nor another. For drivers, the kerbstones on either side of the road define the boundaries of 'normal' motoring. For anyone to veer onto the footpath or into the hedge would show decidedly 'abnormal' behaviour! We have already said that most variables which can be measured show some degree of variation. What is particularly interesting about variation is that, more often than not, the pattern of variation is fairly predictable. A good illustration of this was the beer barrels example in Chapter 1, where the data gave a surprising picture when graphed. In the next activity you will be asked to look at a collection of data and predict where they came from just by thinking about the shape of the distribution.

Look at the stemplot below. It is based on 40 data items, but you don't yet know what they are. In Activity 4 you will be given a chance to guess. (Note: stemplots are explained on page 40.)

N=40

H=48	4—5688
(high limit)	4—012344
	3—556667788999
	3—01133344
	2—5678899
L=22	2—244
(low limit)	

Figure 5.6   Mystery stemplot

4 MATCHING UP THE DATA

(a) Which of the variables below might this stemplot describe?
(b) If you think that one or more of these variables could *not* be described by this stemplot, say why.

Variables:
(i) speeds of 40 cars (in mile/h) measured inside a 30 mile/h limit zone

  (ii) weights of 40 children in kg (2.2 lb = 1 kg)
 (iii) ages (in years) of 40 people arriving at a
        squash club
 (iv) the heartbeat rate (per 30 seconds) of 40
       adults
  (v) the number of matches in 40 matchboxes
       (average contents 52).

● COMMENTS

The mystery stemplot could easily be (i). Note that if the
stemplot had been drawn from variable (i), this would imply that
most people were exceeding the speed limit. Is it likely that
something around three quarters of them exceeded the speed
limit? Well, it rather depends where the survey was taken. If the
speeds were measured just inside the speed limit signs on a long
stretch of open road, then this is quite possible.

The weights of the 40 children (variable (ii)) are only likely to be
the mystery stemplot if the children were around 12 years of
age.

The spread of values on the mystery stemplot (lowest 22 to
highest 48) may be rather narrow for it to represent variable (iii).
I would expect more teenagers and children as well as a few 50-
and 60-year-olds to attend the squash club.

On average the human heart beats at a rate of 70–80 times a
minute in an average healthy adult. I would have expected,
therefore, a distribution whose average was around 35 beats per
30 seconds which is true of the mystery stemplot values.
However, this rate will vary with the amount of exercise taken
and no indication is given of how much variation there is between
individuals or for the same individual on different days.

Finally variable (v) is also unlikely as clearly the mystery
stemplot values are too low.

What these five variables share is that, when a number of
measures are taken of any one of them, they all have this 'middle
of the road' quality. For example, most people's heartbeat rates
will be somewhere in the middle, around 35 beats per 30
seconds. Only a few will be at the extremes with very high or

very low rates. Drawn as a histogram, then, this common type of variation will look like this:

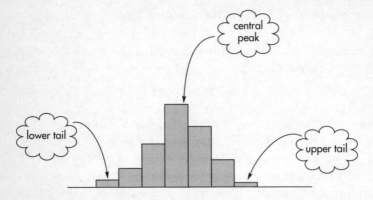

Figure 5.7   A common shape of distribution

This familiar shape could be described as having a *central peak* and *tails* at the extreme values.

However, although all the five examples in Activity 4 will probably show this general shape, variables (iii) and (v) may well differ in other respects. Distributions more typical of these variables have been drawn as stemplots below.

N=40
_____

H=62 6—2
        5—679
        5—34
        4—568
        4—01344
        3—5667789
        3—011334
        2—56799
        2—244
        1—679
L=12 1—24
_____

Figure 5.8   Stemplot showing a typical distribution of ages of squash club players

N=40

H=58 5— 55556677788
      5— 0000011112222223333344444444
      4— 989
L=48

Figure 5.9   Stemplot showing a typical distribution of the number of matches in 40 boxes, whose average contents are claimed to be 52 matches

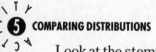

5 COMPARING DISTRIBUTIONS

Look at the stemplots which describe the ages of squash players and the contents of matchboxes.

Explain in your own words how and why they differ from the mystery stemplot referred to in Activity 4.

● **COMMENTS**

Taking the ages of squash players first, you will probably have noticed that the central peak of this distribution is similar to that in the mystery stemplot (about 35). What is different is that the age range of squash club players is much wider than for the mystery stemplot. The *range* of a distribution is usually defined as the largest value minus the smallest value.

So the range in the mystery stemplot is: $48 - 22 = 26$
The range in the squash age data is: $62 - 12 = 50$

The matchbox data are also centrally peaked, but these differ in *two* important respects from the mystery stemplot. Firstly, the values are more narrowly spread. With these data, the range is $58 - 48 = 10$. However, with matchboxes, the central value is no longer around 35. If it were, we would be very unhappy with the claim on each box that, 'Average contents = 52 matches'!

A major question for you to think about here is what is meant by the 'middle 95%' of these distributions. Figure 5.10 overleaf gives a good impression of what this refers to. You will notice that the 5% which lies *outside* this range has been split between the two tails, leaving 2½% of the values in each tail.

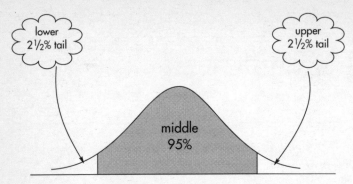

Figure 5.10   A Normal curve

The idea of the middle 95% crops up in all sorts of situations. For example, in October 1988, the Cardinal of Turin revealed to the world that the famous Turin shroud, which many had believed to have been wrapped around Jesus' body in AD 33, was a fake. A fragment of the shroud had been carbon-dated and the tests indicated that the shroud was of medieval origin, making it a much more recent relic than the time of Jesus.

But wasn't it possible that the tests were inaccurate? Well, yes, it was. No test has perfect accuracy but on this occasion the scientists were able to state the degree of accuracy of their results. The statement claimed, 'a 95% likelihood that the 14 foot linen was made between AD 1260 and AD 1390, and a 99% likelihood that it was made between AD 1230 and AD 1420'. Clearly their 'best' estimate would be exactly in the middle of these two ranges — making a likely date of AD 1325. The scientists' estimate could be expressed in a diagram, as follows:

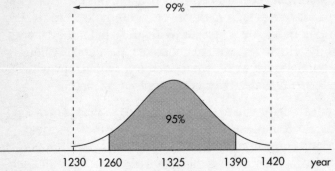

Figure 5.11   'Likelihood' estimates

So what chance is there of the 'true' date being around AD 33?
To answer this, you would have to extend the graph to the left for
another 1200 years or so. The likelihood involved would be
represented by the tiny tail to the left of this point — which
probably puts it beyond all reasonable doubt!

6 THE MIDDLE 95%

Write down the values which mark out the middle 95% of the data
showing the ages of the squash players in figure 5.8.
(Hint: $\frac{1}{40}$th $= 2\frac{1}{2}$%.)

● **COMMENTS**

The upper and lower tails of this distribution *each* contain $2\frac{1}{2}$%
(that is, 1 out of 40) of the values. The middle 95% of the values,
therefore, are contained within the ages 14 to 59 inclusive.

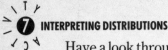

7 INTERPRETING DISTRIBUTIONS

Have a look through this last section (subtitled 'Comparing Distributions') and note down the main points to watch out for when interpreting data in a stemplot or histogram.

● **COMMENTS**

Stemplots, tally charts and histograms give a much better picture of the overall distribution of the variable than you can get by just looking at the raw data. In particular they allow us to see:

(a) whether the distribution has a central peak (some distributions have several peaks or a peak which is not central)

(b) roughly what is the middle or average value of the distribution

(c) how widely spread the values are (the range is just one measure of spread). The spread of the middle 95% of the values is also useful.

SUMMARY

That ends this chapter on spreads and distributions. The main points covered were as follows.

● Variation — no two people will be exactly the same height, nor will two bags of crisps weigh exactly the same. Anything which can be measured will show some degree of variation.

● Distribution — if you measured the heights of, say 100 people, or weighed 100 bags of crisps, a better picture of the variation could be obtained by displaying the results in a stemplot, tally chart or histogram. The 'shape' you get is the distribution, and it gives you a more precise picture of the nature of the variation.

● Range — this is a simple measure of how widely *spread* the distribution is. Another way of indicating the spread is to state the limits of the middle 95% of the distribution.

FOLLOW-UP EXERCISES

1 Suppose that 30 similar bags of crisps were weighed and the
. results plotted as a histogram.
   (a) What general shape would you expect the histogram to
       have?
   (b) Identify two possible factors which might account for the
       variation in the weights of the bags.
   (c) What would the tallest column of the histogram tell you?

2 Suppose a sample of size 30 was taken of each of the
   following and plotted as a histogram or stemplot. Which
   distribution has the wider spread:

   (a) (i) the weights of 30 eggs taken from a Size 3 egg
             box
     or (ii) the weight of 30 eggs taken from a hen house
   (b) (i) the weights of 30 eggs taken from a zoo
     or (ii) the weights of 30 eggs taken from a hen house
   (c) (i) the capacities of 30 one litre measuring jugs
     or (ii) the capacities of 30 different teapots
   (d) (i) the body temperatures of 30 people
     or (ii) the air temperatures taken over 30 days
             throughout the year?

6 Selecting the Sample

This chapter is about how and why we sometimes select a sample to help get a picture of what some wider population is like. Note that in common usage, the word 'population' is usually taken to refer to a large group of people or animals. In Statistics this word has a much wider meaning and can refer to practically any large group of things. For example, in Statistics we talk about a 'population of electric light bulbs', 'a population of kettles' and so on. If we wish to find out more about light bulbs (perhaps how long they last) or about kettles (for example, how long they take to boil), it is clearly not practical to test the entire population. Indeed, in the case of light bulbs, which are 'tested to destruction', there wouldn't be any left over after testing to sell in the shops! The sensible solution is to take smaller samples from the overall populations and test these. The skill of the statistician is to choose the samples so that they fairly represent the population from which they were taken.

Key terms: *sample, population, representative, bias, opinion polls, questionnaire.*

JUST TYPICAL

You won't catch me shopping there — my brother bought a watch from them and he had nothing but trouble from it.

I hate Italian food. I had a pasta once and I was ill for days!

My grandfather smoked 40 cigarettes a day all his life and he's the healthiest person I know.

I've always opposed making the wearing of seat belts compulsory since I read about that woman who got trapped when her car caught fire.

No doubt you have taken part in conversations like these many times yourself. We all make decisions about where we go for our holidays, which shop to use, what we eat, and so on, on the basis of past experience. However, sometimes past experience can be very fleeting, or perhaps very untypical. This may be misleading and cause us to make 'false generalisations'. The four quotes above are examples where the generalisation has been made on the basis of a single experience. However, for most of the decisions which we make in life, a single experience is rarely enough.

You have already met the idea of variation in the previous chapter. Variation is the word we use to describe the notion that no two things are exactly the same; watches vary in the time they keep, and similarly the quality of the pasta may vary greatly from one Italian restaurant to another. *Your* grandfather may well have remained healthy despite a lifetime's cigarette smoking, but sadly, many other people's grandfathers have not. Finally, to take the last quote given above, car seat belts have probably caused some injuries, but have certainly prevented others. When deciding whether they are a 'good thing' overall, we have to weigh up the costs with the benefits. Quoting a single experience fails to take this wider view which takes account of the variation that you might expect to occur.

In the same way, a group of people chosen at random will probably have widely varying heights, tastes, opinions, and so on. If we wanted to find out more about that group of people, it would be foolish to choose just one person at random to be representative of them. We know from everyday experience that it is necessary to sample more widely in order to gain a clearer impression of everyone being considered.

Since this whole chapter is concerned with this central idea of why, what and how we should sample, have a go at Activity 1, which will help you to get a better sense of what these key questions are about.

① INVESTIGATING YOUR MEDICAL FACILITIES

Suppose that you wish to find out what people think about the medical facilities in your area.

    (a) What might be wrong with asking just one person (i.e. choosing a sample size of one)?

    (b) How many people (i.e. what size of sample) should you choose so that you hear views which are *completely* representative of the entire population in your area?

● COMMENTS

    (a) First of all, the problem with asking just one person, i.e. choosing a sample of size one, is that the person you choose will not be able to represent the wide range of different views about medical facilities in the region. Various groups of people (for example, mothers with young children, elderly people, young people, people without transport, people living in poverty, healthy people, chronically sick people, and so on) will have different needs and very different experiences of the medical facilities available. If you hope to take account of all these needs and experiences, you will need to take a sample size greater than one!

    (b) The only way that you can guarantee *complete* representativeness is to 'sample' the entire population. Since this is rarely practical, the point to emerge from this is that a sample can never be completely representative of the population from which it was taken.

So, basically, people sample in order to get a clearer picture of a wider population. A 'good' sample is one which is as representative of that population as possible. For example, if you are 'sampling' a pot of soup before serving it to your guests, you'd probably give the pot a good stir first to ensure that your sample spoonful is typical of the rest. However, sometimes sampling is carried out in a way that is clearly biased.

2 BIASED SAMPLING

Try to think of a few examples where samples have been selected which are definitely *not* typical of the wider population.

● COMMENTS

There are many examples in everyday life where biased samples are taken. For example, the apples displayed in a greengrocer's window were probably a biased sample selected from the total 'population' of apples in the shop. Similarly, judging students on the basis of their performance in a single examination is an example of biased sampling. (There are many variable factors which affect a student's examination performance; for example, which particular topics are covered in the examination, whether it is an essay style, multiple choice, oral exam and so on.) One of the most famous examples of biased sampling took place just before the American presidential election in 1936. An American magazine took a huge sample of ten million people, of whom two million replied to the questionnaire. Their replies suggested a massive victory for the Republican candidate. In the event the Democrat, Franklin D. Roosevelt, won with a huge majority. So what went wrong? Well, the problem lay in their sampling procedure. The questionnaires were sent to subscribers to the magazine, as well as to a list of names chosen from the telephone directory. If you didn't read the magazine or own a telephone, you weren't asked. So despite the fact that a huge sample was taken, it would seem that it was not representative of the population as a whole. People who bought the magazine or owned telephones were rather better off than average and this was a key factor in terms of voting intentions.

On a lighter note, just before the American presidential election in 1988, a local radio station hit on an original way of polling their listeners' opinions about their preferences between the two candidates. First of all those who favoured George Bush were asked to flush their toilet. A few seconds later the same request was made for supporters of Michael Dukakis. A meter on the city water pressure was read on each occasion and the results indicated a preference for Dukakis by about 10%. Clearly this type of toilet polling technique is both quick and cheap, but in the light of the eventual result, its predictive accuracy leaves a lot to be desired! You will have to decide for yourself whether the failure of the approach was due to sample bias or inaccuracy in the measurement of water pressure.

In general, larger samples tend to be more accurate, but of course, large samples cost money. Sampling is therefore a balancing act between accuracy on the one hand and cost and effort on the other.

Another factor that has already been mentioned is the speed of the sampling process. With some types of data, speed may not matter very much, but, increasingly, people want information that is up-to-date. A good example of this is the data on which the pop record charts are compiled. Let's face it — who cares which records people liked *last* week? In order to ensure that they are polling today's preferences, Radio 1 uses an extremely rapid sampling method in their 'Chartbeat' survey. Listeners get a chance to hear 10 new record releases and can place their vote for the record of their choice directly by dialling to the BBC computer. The final digit dialled (a number between 0 and 9) automatically records a vote for the record corresponding to that number. Using this technique, the BBC can compile a poll from around 5 000 listeners in a matter of minutes. Similar techniques are sometimes used in television programmes to poll viewers' opinions and we can probably expect more of this sort of polling in the future. Of course, there is no real guarantee that the 5 000 people phoning in to 'Chartbeat' are representative of the entire record-buying population. You might like to pause now and think about how representative, or not, this sample might be.

Still on the theme of representativeness, have a look through the advertisements for cinema or theatre performances below, which quote reviewers' comments.

'the best musical in town' *Daily Express*
'riotous and splendidly sung—spiffing' *Daily Mail*
'a delight from beginning to end . . . not to be missed' *Times Educational Supplement*
'yet another winner' *The Scotsman*

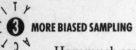

③ MORE BIASED SAMPLING

How much care do you think has been taken by the advertisers to ensure that these quotes are representative of all the various comments made by all the reviewers from different newspapers?

● COMMENTS

Are you kidding?! This is another example where in practice the conventional rules of statistical sampling do not apply.

To end this section, read through the following rather uncomplimentary review of the Philip Glass stage work and then have a go at Activity 4.

GLASS WITH AN EARTH-SHATTERING EFFECT

The making of the Representative for Planet 8: English National Opera, London Coliseum

Philip Glass's new stage work, receiving its British première here, is that rare species, an operatic 'green', a composition for our ecologically conscious times...

... The story is taken from a mystic science fiction novel by Doris Lessing, who has also written the opera's libretto.

When we first see Planet 8 it is green, temperate and fruitful, but an ice age brings global disaster to its complacent people.

The message is clear — we are all representatives of what the programme calls 'our piece of planetary real estate'. Let us abuse our inheritance at our peril.

But a theme for our time does not necessarily ensure an evening of compelling music-theatre and, unfortunately, the message came across with as much real chill as a damp downpour.

Harry Silverstein's static shuffling production perfectly matches the laboured pace of the composer's score. For Glass himself seems to have an ice age too — his throbbing pulsating style now frozen into an endlessly repetitious pattern...

... One sympathises with the cast. This may be a boost for ecology but it is an apology for an opera.

David Gillard

Source: *Daily Mail*, 16th November, 1988, p. 38

④ SELECTIVE SAMPLING

Imagine that you are responsible for promoting ticket sales to this opera. Choose two phrases from the review which you might want to include in your advertising material.

● COMMENTS

A well-known trick by unscrupulous theatre managers is to take a phrase entirely out of context so that it appears to be complimentary. Here are two highly complimentary (and highly misleading!) extracts taken from the *Daily Mail* review above.

'an evening of compelling music-theatre'
'throbbing pulsating style' *Daily Mail*

But despite these examples where sampling bias is deliberate, most people seek to avoid bias, if at all possible, when taking a sample. How, then, can we ensure that a sample is representative of the overall population? I have already stated that it can never be completely representative (except in highly artificial cases). However, there are two general principles on sampling which will ensure that your sample is reasonably representative. These are:

(a) *choose a fairly large sample* (i.e. don't just dip your finger into the soup but taste a whole spoonful!)

(b) *Make sure that the sample you choose is typical* — i.e. that it fairly represents all the important features of the population (this corresponds to giving the soup a good stir before tasting it).

SAMPLING OPINIONS

One of the trickiest tasks that you may have to perform in Statistics is to sample what people's opinions are about certain issues. Opinion polling is a huge topic and we won't have time to go into it in any detail here. Instead we'll look at just one particular aspect — designing a questionnaire.

5 IT'S YOUR VERDICT

IT'S YOUR VERDICT

1 I believe that capital punishment should be brought back for the following categories of murder:
Children ☐   Police ☐   Terrorism ☐   All murders ☐

2 Life sentences for serious crimes like murder and rape should carry a minimum term of:
20 years ☐   25 years ☐

3 The prosecution should have the right of appeal against sentences they consider to be too lenient. ☐

* Tick the boxes of those statements you agree with and then post the coupon to:
VIOLENT BRITAIN, *Daily Star*, 33 St. Bride St., London EC4A 4AY.

This 'questionnaire' appeared in the *Daily Star* newspaper on 11th February, 1985, under the headline 'We've had ENOUGH!'.

(a) Have a go yourself at completing the questionnaire.
(b) Note down some criticisms of the way it has been designed.

● **COMMENTS**

What is remarkable about this 'questionnaire' is the restricted range of choices offered in the responses. For example, there are no boxes available for you to tick if you don't believe in the death penalty (question 1), or think that longer prison sentences won't necessarily solve the problem of violent crime (question 2). Also, placing it amongst headlines such as, 'We've had enough!', 'My mother's killer runs free' and 'Hang the Gunmen' is likely to bias the response. Not surprisingly, of the 40 000 readers who replied, 86.33% favoured restoring capital punishment for murder, 92% wanted a 25-year minimum sentence for serious crimes of violence and 95.58% supported the right of appeal to the prosecution against sentences they considered to be too lenient. These findings contrast sharply with other more reputable surveys which consistently suggest that most people, including victims of violent crime, would prefer a system of community service and compensation to victims rather than longer prison sentences. (Data are available on these questions from Marplan and the Prison Reform Trust.)

There are many examples of questionnaires which unfairly limit the responses which you might wish to make. Sometimes companies publish advertisements disguised as questionnaires. For example, here are two made-up questions which a telephone company might use as a subtle way of promoting their product.

Question 1
The more you think about it, the more you realise just how vital the telephone is in your life. Do you:
(a) Only use it when you need to?
(b) Use it extensively for both social and work purposes?
(c) Feel extremely threatened by it and would much rather write long letters or communicate with everyone face to face?

Question 2
You have an important client whom you need to talk to on the
telephone. Do you:
(a) Take your time, choose a comfortable seat and dial slowly?
(b) Walk around the office to build up your courage and then make the
call?
(c) Panic, give up and go off for a drink instead?

Admittedly questionnaires like these are meant as a bit of fun,
but there are some interesting features nevertheless. For
example, notice how question 1 isn't a question at all, but is a
piece of direct propaganda about the importance of a telephone.
Secondly you will notice that the responses (a) and (b) in both
questions are reasonably sensible and involve using the
telephone in some fairly standard way, while (c) responses are
totally loopy. So the message is clear, there are two sorts of
people — those who use their telephones sensibly and people
who are complete nutcases!

To end this section we will take another look at questionnaire
design.

6 HOW HEALTHY ARE YOU?

(a) Quickly fill in your responses to the questionnaire on health
below.

Question 1	How healthy are you?	....
Question 2	Do you think you are fit?	....
Question 3	What sort of food do you eat?	....
Question 4	What exercise do you take and how often?	....
Question 5	Are you overweight?	....
Question 6	Will you agree to take part in this survey?	YES

(b) Give several reasons why you think this was not a very
well-designed questionnaire.

● COMMENTS

No doubt you found some of these questions difficult to answer.
All in all, as questionnaires go, it was pretty dreadful! The following
list notes some of the points you may have come up with.

1   There was no indication overall as to why these questions were being asked. Generally people like to be convinced that a survey is useful before they will co-operate by filling in a questionnaire.

2   The questions weren't ordered in any sensible way. The worst example of this is leaving question 6 (Will you agree to take part in this survey?) till the end.

3   Most of the questions were impossible to answer. For example, question 5 (Are you overweight?) provides no help with a definition of what 'overweight' means. Some thin people *feel* overweight and some well-rounded people don't.

4   For some of the questions there wasn't enough space on the paper to give a complete answer (for example, question 4).

5   Questions which require a 'yes/no' answer, such as questions 5 and 6, should be both clear and consistent in how they are worded and set out. For example, if people are expected to tick a box, there should be *three* options ('Yes', 'No' and 'Don't know'), with three corresponding boxes, and an instruction alongside stating 'Please tick'.

6   Finally, questions should be chosen and phrased in such a way that the person carrying out the survey can *make use of the information collected*. This means avoiding asking questions that are irrelevant, vague, impossible or offensive. Remember that a badly thought-out questionnaire with no clear purpose is only a waste of everyone's time!

To end this section, here is a short check list of some of the dos and don'ts of questionnaire design.

(a) Explain why you are carrying out the survey.
(b) Order the questions sensibly.
(c) Don't ask questions that are impossible to answer.
(d) Leave room on the questionnaire for alternative or fuller answers where appropriate.
(e) Only ask necessary questions.
(f) Remember that a badly worded or offensive questionnaire gives polling a bad name.

Most of the examples in this chapter have been of bad practice in sampling. But why are there no examples of good survey questions? It is actually quite difficult to provide an example of a 'good' questionnaire. This is because each questionnaire is designed to meet a particular need and it is impossible to assess the quality of each question without knowing why it has been asked and how the responses will be analysed and interpreted.

SUMMARY

In this chapter we looked at how estimates about populations can be made by looking only at a sample of the population. However, the estimate will only be accurate if the sample chosen is representative. The best hope of ensuring that your sample is representative is to take a reasonably large sample size, and, if possible, to choose the items fairly so that each item has an equal chance of selection.

FOLLOW-UP EXERCISES

1   Why do people bother to take samples at all?

2   What is the key characteristic of a 'good' sample?

3   How could you select a 'good' sample from a population?

4   The table below shows four examples of inappropriate samples which have been selected in order to make an estimate of the corresponding population. Indicate where the sampling procedure is faulty in each case and suggest how it could be improved.

Population	Sample
(a) National voting preferences	Workmen on a building site
(b) National earnings	Group of shoppers in the High Street on Monday afternoon
(c) Total annual shop takings	Takings each Saturday over 12 weeks
(d) A householder's telephone bill	Telephone calls made between 9 and 10 p.m. each day

7 Deciding on Differences

The main reason that we ever bother to collect and analyse data at all is because we want to decide whether certain things are similar or different. It is fairly easy to see whether two numbers differ. What is much harder is to decide whether or not the differences between them are worth taking seriously and the result wasn't just a fluke. The main aim of this chapter is to help raise the distinction in your mind between a 'difference' and a 'significant difference'.

Key terms: *population pyramid, back-to-back stemplot.*

DO THE ANSWERS FIT THE QUESTIONS?

Just how honest are you? For example, how do you feel about milkmen overcharging their customers, or employees 'fiddling' their expenses claims? These are just two out of a number of questions asked in the *British Social Attitudes Survey* which is published each year. This book provides interesting statistics about people's attitudes on a wide range of questions, such as honesty, education, sex, politics and so on. Before looking at some of the statistics, spend a few minutes thinking about your own attitudes to honesty by doing the activity below.

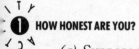 **1** HOW HONEST ARE YOU?

(a) Suppose you found £5 in the street, would you:

    (i) leave it
    (ii) hand it in to the police
    (iii) pocket it?

Now answer the same question if the sum of money was £100.

(b) Look at the data given in the following table which shows how a sample of people responded to this question.

Write down in one sentence what you think they reveal about
people's honesty.

Answer	Amount found £5 note %	£20 note %	£100 in notes %
Leave it	1	1	1
Hand it in to the police	27	48	75
Pocket it	69	48	21
Other	3	3	3

Source: R. Jowell, S. Witherspoon and L. Brooks, *British Social Attitudes: 5th Report*, Aldershot, Gower, 1988, p. 5

Figure 7.1   Honesty survey

● COMMENTS

The main feature of this table seems to be that people do behave
differently with different amounts of money. In general, the
larger the amount of money they find, the less likely they are to
pocket it and the more likely they are to hand it in to the police.
So, if you believe these figures, there is no real difficulty in
'deciding on differences' here. Whereas about 70% would pocket
the £5 note, only about 20% would pocket the £100. When
differences are as large as this, the conclusion is obvious. The
difference between 70% and 20% is clearly 'significant' and no
further statistical work is needed. However, I wonder if these
figures surprise you. Would you have expected roughly seven
out of ten people to pocket a £5 note which they found in the
street? The proportion does seem rather high. Perhaps the
survey got it wrong. The rest of this section will look at whether
we can really trust the data in figure 7.1.

First of all, you might question the sample of people asked. How
large a sample was it? Were the people questioned typical of the
population as a whole? Perhaps the respondents didn't give
thoughtful or honest answers? Clearly we are into Chapter 6
territory here, questioning the sampling procedure used. But
these are such important questions that they are likely to crop up
at some stage in any statistical investigation and so we will look at
them again here.

So, there are important questions here on the sampling methods used and the questions asked in the survey. Contained in the introduction to the *British Social Attitudes* book, there seems to be an answer to these concerns. Here it explains exactly how long each interview lasted and how many people were sampled:

> [The book's] primary source of data is an hour-long annual interview survey . . . among a probability sample of 3000 people nationwide.

So it seems that each respondent was interviewed for one hour. This must make it less likely that glib or deliberately dishonest answers were given. The sample size of 3000 is indeed large and, since it has been based on a nationwide survey, is at least representative in terms of the geographic regions of the country. (Further information in the book also reveals that it is balanced in terms of age, sex, social class, occupation and political voting preferences.)

Since the survey seems to pass the test of using 'correct' sampling methods, we can now be reasonably confident that the attitudes revealed in figure 7.1 are indeed representative of the whole population. However, you may still feel unhappy that so many people would have pocketed the £5 note. Wouldn't most people be embarrassed to be seen picking up a £5 in the street and putting it in their pocket? Well, in fact the question as stated in Activity 1 is not how it was worded in the original survey. Here is the full question:

> Suppose you are alone in an empty street: no one is likely to come by and see you. There is a £5 note lying on the pavement. Would you leave it there, pick it up and hand it in at the police station, or pick it up and pocket it?

You might like to consider whether you would have responded differently to *this* question than to the one given in Activity 1.

An important statistical point to come out of this example is that you need to know the *exact wording* of the question asked in order to appreciate the significance of the findings. Newspapers often provide catchy headlines and brief summaries of research findings where the exact wording of the questions that have been asked is not clear.

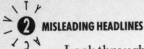

2 MISLEADING HEADLINES

Look through some newspapers until you find a report of a recent
opinion poll finding. (You can spot these with headlines like 'Poll
Shows . . .' or 'Survey Reveals . . .'.) Try to work out what the
exact wording of the question was. Now see if you can alter the
wording of the headline slightly to give a different interpretation
to the results.

● COMMENTS

Here is an example of a misleading headline, based on an opinion
poll with a sample size of one. In 1985, just after the Brighton
bombing incident (where the Conservative party conference
hotel was bombed by the IRA), a Conservative MP who had been
injured in the blast was asked to comment. He said that he
opposed the death penalty for terrorists on the grounds that this
could make them into heroic martyrs but was in favour of the
death penalty for professional criminals who kill. The next day
the *Daily Star* covered the story with the headline: 'HANG THE
GUNMEN: that's the view of a victim of Brighton's bomb blast.'
You might like to think about whether this headline was a fair
summary of what he really said. Let's return now to the central
theme of this chapter — deciding on differences.

In the first example we looked at in this section on people's
honesty, the 'difference' in question was obvious. It was quite
clear from the data given that how people respond to finding
money lying in the street varies, depending on the amount of
money they find. However, as you will see shortly, deciding on
differences in data is not always so straightforward.

PROBLEMS OF MEASUREMENT

3 DIFFERENCES IN HONESTY

(a) Do older people tend to be more or less honest than younger
people?
(b) Are women generally more honest than men?

Make a note of which answer you would expect to these
questions and then spend a few minutes thinking about a possible

statistical investigation you might carry out to help you decide whether you were right. Try to use the four PCAI stages to organise your ideas.

● **COMMENTS**

Stage P — Pose the question.

Since the questions have already been posed for you in Activity 3, we can pass through this stage fairly quickly. However, it's worth thinking about some of the difficulties of definition and measurement which lie ahead. This means being clear about the sort of factors which the questions will be dealing with. Question (a) deals with *age* and *honesty*, while question (b) is concerned with *gender* and *honesty*. There are clearly no serious problems in measuring age and gender (age is a continuous variable, measured in years, while gender is discrete, having two categories of female and male). The difficulty is how to measure something as vague as 'honesty'. There is certainly no neat way of classifying people into the categories 'honest' and 'dishonest'. Equally, how would you rate a person's honesty on a number scale from 1 to 10? However, there are several possible ways of tackling this problem. One approach might be to look at the statistics of people convicted of criminal offences. The chart in figure 7.2 overleaf shows the pattern of criminal offences committed by males and females separately between the ages of 10 and 20.

There are two obvious 'differences' which this graph shows up. The first is a clear link between age and crime. For both males and females they reach a peak of offending at around the age of 15 or 16 years and then it falls away again as they get older. What these graphs fail to do, of course, is explain *why* these patterns exist. Why is it that young people are most likely to get into trouble with the police at around the age of 15 or 16? You might like to spend a few minutes now thinking about this.

(One possibility might be that there is a big difference between who commits crimes and who gets caught committing crimes. It could be, for example, that the younger criminals are more likely to get caught.)

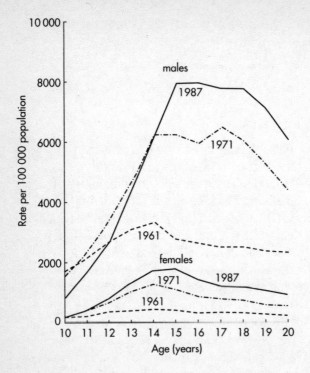

Source: Government Statistical Service, *Social Trends 19*, London, HMSO, 1989, p. 191

Figure 7.2   Offenders aged under 21 accused of indictable offences, by sex and age

The second pattern which emerges from the graphs is the large difference between male and female crime rates. Does this suggest, then, that women are more law abiding than men? The answer to this question seems to be yes! At all ages, the vast majority of crimes, and particularly crimes of violence, are committed by men. For example, out of an average prison population of 56 400 people in England and Wales in 1987, roughly 96% of them were men. (Source: Central Statistical Office, *Social Trends 19*, London, HMSO, 1989, table 12.12.) The explanation for these differences lies beyond the scope of a statistics textbook, but, again, you might like to spend a few minutes now thinking about why these gender differences in criminal behaviour might exist.

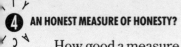

④ AN HONEST MEASURE OF HONESTY?

How good a measure do you think these crime statistics are of people's honesty in general? Make a note of any drawbacks you can think of.

● COMMENTS

We need to be aware that just looking at prison statistics is to focus on only 0.1% (i.e. one in a thousand) of the whole population. Furthermore, it isn't reasonable to assume that the prison population contains a representative sample of the population as a whole, particularly in their attitudes to honesty. Finally, before you get too smug about your own honesty, the term 'honesty' has a much broader meaning than committing the sort of crimes for which you might be sent to jail. A person's honesty is probably as much to do with small things like lying and not revealing that you've been given too much change as it is with robbing banks. Clearly these things are very hard to measure, except, perhaps, by asking a representative sample of people directly about their attitudes to honesty, as has been done in the British Attitudes Survey.

In this section we have raised a question of whether there are gender differences in terms of honesty. To end the section you are asked to check out gender differences in two other respects.

⑤ COMPARING THE SEXES

Using the four PCAI stages of a statistical investigation, plan how you might investigate the following questions:

(a) Do women live longer than men?
(b) Are there more women or men in public life (i.e. are well-known public figures)?

● COMMENTS

The first of these questions will be investigated in the following section, so there will be no further comments given here. However, it is very important that you think particularly about the P and C stages of the exercise above before reading on. Otherwise you will not have a chance to consider what data you might need to collect to help you answer these sorts of questions.

DO WOMEN LIVE LONGER THAN MEN?

We start this section with the question 'Do women live longer than men?'. Now clearly it isn't the case that all women live longer than all men — some women live longer than some men, and some men live longer than some women. But statistical investigations are about observing overall trends, not dealing with absolutes. Our commonsense observation of the world suggests that we tend to see more elderly women around than elderly men. However, one person's 'common sense' doesn't make for a very convincing case. As Sherlock Holmes once said, 'Data, give me data Watson! I can't make bricks without straw!'. If we are to verify the claim that women live longer, we need to start by deciding what data would be most helpful. One possibility is to turn to an official government publication such as *Social Trends*. There you can find the following data describing the age and sex structure of the population:

	0–4	5–14	15–29	30–44	45–59	60–74	75–84	85+	All ages
Males (millions)	1.9	3.6	6.9	5.8	4.6	3.6	1.1	0.2	27.7
Females (millions)	1.8	3.4	6.6	5.8	4.6	4.4	1.9	0.6	29.2

Source: Central Statistical Office, *Social Trends 19*, London, HMSO, 1989, table 1.2 (from OPCS data)

Figure 7.3   Age and sex structure of the UK population, mid-year estimate for 1987

6 BROKEN DOWN BY AGE AND SEX . . .

In the table above, how do you account for the differences in the numbers of people in each grouping?

● COMMENTS

There are several reasons for the differences which appear in this table. First of all, you may have been surprised to see that there seem to be nearly twice as many children in the second age band (5–14 years) as the first (0–4 years). But you must be careful here! Note that these age bands are not of equal width, so you are not comparing like with like. Secondly, it is clear from these figures that there are indeed more elderly women than men (about three times as many women in the 85+ category as men) which does seem to confirm that women do live longer.

These figures raise a number of interesting questions about the patterns in the population as a whole. For example, even when we take account of the different widths of age bands, there are still different numbers of people at each age. For example, there were more people born in 1946 than in 1942 in the UK. Why should this be? Well, for a start, the death rates and birth rates vary over time. Clearly during the last war with so many men away fighting, the birth rates fell and the death rates rose. Then, for the two or three years immediately after the war, birth rates rose again sharply, and this produced a 'bulge' or 'boom' in the population. In the USA the generation born just after the war is often referred to as the 'baby boomers'. One interesting thing about a population bulge is that when the baby boomers start having children themselves 20 to 25 years later, then, simply because there are more of them, a second population bulge is produced.

Population bulges also occur for many other reasons. For example, rising house prices and high mortgage rates can discourage young couples from having children. Fashions in 'ideal' family size can also change over time. (In the 1970s, many couples favoured two children as ideal, but in the 1980s there seemed to be a trend towards having three.) It isn't at all clear how and why these trends occur, and you might like to spend a few minutes now thinking about this question.

7 EXPLORING THE PYRAMIDS

The diagram in figure 7.4 overleaf is called a population pyramid. Note any particular features of this chart which interest you and try to explain them.

● COMMENTS

A population pyramid takes its name from its shape, which looks more or less like a pyramid. The reason for this shape is that there are fewer elderly people in the population so the population graph increasingly narrows at the top. For populations which are

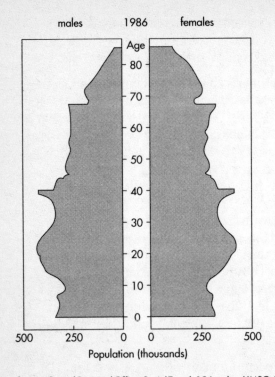

males   1986   females

Source: Central Statistical Office, *Social Trends 19*, London, HMSO, 1989, p. 25

Figure 7.4   Population of England and Wales, 1986

growing, the largest age band will be the youngest (the bottom part of the chart).

There are many interesting features in this chart. Firstly, note the baby boomers (both male and female) around the age of 40. Since the data refer to 1986, this means that this group were born around 1946. (The Second World War lasted from 1939 to 1945.) And what of the children of these baby boomers? Well, there is certainly a wide bulge between the ages of 15 and 30 years and some of these could be sons and daughters of the post-war boomers. However, this bulge is so large and wide that there are almost certainly other factors at work. Another significant 'blip' appears in the 67 to 70 year age group. As before, it isn't hard to relate this to the effects of the First World War (1914 to 1918). Finally, the patterns at the very top of the

pyramid confirm what we have already seen from figure 7.4 —
that there are indeed many more elderly women than elderly
men in the population.

So far we have investigated the question of whether women tend
to live longer than men by using published 'official' statistics. A
different approach would be to look through the death columns in
a daily newspaper and try to see if there are patterns in the age at
death of those listed. The following data for 40 males and 40
females were taken from *The Independent* in February 1989.

Males

72	89	80	74	68	73	64	62	73	86
77	77	52	79	71	86	01	91	63	82
77	93	82	23	80	61	90	77	87	82
79	61	87	74	82	74	74	79	62	65

Females

84	31	100	70	95	67	96	73	71	83
102	94	83	89	82	76	92	76	84	68
70	85	67	80	95	93	86	77	95	82
82	95	42	91	91	78	81	91	87	84

Source: *The Independent*, data taken over several days in February 1989, Gazette page

Figure 7.5   Age at death (years) of 40 males and 40 females

8 PLOTTING DEATHS

(a) How representative to you think these samples are of the
'age at death' of the population as a whole?

(b)

Age at death (years)

Women	Men (mean 72.72)
	10:
	9:013
	8:00222266779
	7:123344447777999
	6:12245778
	5:2

Outliers 1, 23

Source: *The Independent*, data taken over several days in February 1989, Gazette page

Figure 7.6   Stemplot showing data from figure 7.5

The data for males have been plotted on a stemplot in figure 7.6 and the mean has been calculated. Draw a second stemplot for the female ages back-to-back to the one for males in the space provided in figure 7.6. Also calculate the mean age at death for women.

(c) Is there clear evidence here that women live longer than men?

● **COMMENTS**

(a) One might expect that readers of *The Independent*, being, in general, rather middle class and better-off than average, would have a longer than average life expectancy. Another aspect which does not emerge from these data, as shown above, is that there were more males listed in the newspaper death columns than females (about three males per two females). However, there is no obvious reason why these two factors should greatly bias our investigation.

(b) The mean age at death for these 40 females works out to be 81.70 years, which is about nine years older than that of the men. Assuming you were able to complete all of part (b), this difference is also clearly evident in the back-to-back stemplot.

(c) The evidence of these two samples suggests strongly that, on average, women *do* live longer than men. If the difference between the lifespans of men and women could be proved, then this would be described as a 'statistically significant difference' between men's and women's age at death. The calculations involved in deciding whether a difference is, or is not, statistically significant are beyond the scope of this book and we have certainly not *proved* a statistically significant difference here. However, the question of the significance is an important one. It may appear obvious that the mean age at death of females is older than that of males. But what you have to ask yourself is whether, given the fairly large sample sizes of 40, and given the sort of spread of values which we see in the stemplots, this difference in the means was just a fluke. Common sense suggests that the difference isn't a fluke and that the results *are* statistically significant.

SUMMARY

This chapter looked at an important and difficult question in Statistics — how we decide on whether one thing is bigger than another and whether that difference is 'significant'. If a sample of each of the two things you wish to compare is collected, it is usually helpful to compare their distributions graphically by plotting them on a back-to-back stemplot. By comparing the two distributions, this should give you a good intuitive sense of how different they are. However, how can you be sure that if two different samples were collected the same difference would be revealed? To answer this question would require the application of a formal statistical test of significance, which is beyond the scope of this book.

FOLLOW-UP EXERCISES

1   Which of the following would be useful in helping you to decide on differences between two samples:
   (i)   back-to-back stemplot
  (ii)   pie chart
 (iii)   scatterplot
 (iv)   two bar charts (one for each sample)?

2   Consider the following statistical investigation: 'Are the babies born to women who smoke during pregnancy lighter than average?'
  (a)   What sort of data might you need to collect to test whether or not this statement is true?
  (b)   How could you represent your data graphically to help you reach a conclusion?

3   Draw up a checklist of three or four questions that you should ask of yourself before accepting a statement that two groups are significantly different.

8 Cause and Correlation

Correlation is a measure of how strongly two things are related to each other. A common misconception with many people is that having evidence that two things are related somehow proves that one has *caused* the other. This is not true! In short, cause and correlation do not necessarily go together.

Key terms: *positive and negative relationships, strong and weak correlation, cause and effect, projection.*

GETTING INVOLVED IN A RELATIONSHIP

'The more the long time, the littler my balloon grows.'
                                        Carrie (aged 4 years)
'Eddie says that the longer your legs, the faster you can run.'
                                        Carrie (aged 5 years)
'Ah, I see. So the higher the number on the pencil, the harder the lead.'   Carrie (aged 6 years)

People studying Statistics sometimes find the idea of correlation rather difficult. Of course it isn't hard to make something sound very complicated, but the basic idea of correlation is quite simple. However, in order to understand correlation, you do need to be clear in your mind what is meant by saying that two things are *related*. As the three quotations above show, this idea of a relationship is one which Carrie is already getting to grips with.

Carrie's remarks shown above draw attention to three particular relationships. These are:

(a) 'time' with 'balloon size'

(b) 'leg length' with 'running speed'
(c) 'pencil number' with 'the hardness of the lead'.

Let's look a bit more closely now at just how these things relate to each other. When two things are related, like, say, the weight of a bag of tomatoes and its price, the first question to establish is whether the relationship is *positive* or *negative*.

The bag of tomatoes is an example of a direct relationship — as its weight increases, so you would expect to pay more for it. Clearly you would expect to pay *more* money for *more* tomatoes, so a positive relationship can be thought of as the 'more for more' type. A negative relationship is the opposite — that is, it is a 'more for less' sort of relationship. An example of a negative relationship would be the connection between your spending and saving. The *more* you spend, the *less* you are able to save, and vice versa.

1 POSITIVE AND NEGATIVE RELATIONSHIPS

Think about each of Carrie's three statements in turn and try to decide whether they describe positive or negative relationships.

● COMMENTS

The first statement is an example of a negative relationship — as 'time' increases, so the 'balloon size' decreases. The second statement describes a positive relationship — as 'leg length' increases, so 'running speed' increases. Finally, the third statement is also a positive relationship — as the 'pencil number' increases, so the 'lead hardness' increases.

Incidentally, this third statement is only partly true. Carrie's generalisation was based on her experience of the following rather narrow range of pencils:

Softer lead ←   → Harder lead
    H   2H   3H   4H   5H

Carrie's relationship between pencil number and the hardness of the lead breaks down when we look at a fuller range of the pencils available, to include the pencils with soft leads:

Softer lead ←   → Harder lead
    6B 5B 4B 3B 2B B HB F H 2H 3H 4H 5H

So far we've simply expressed the nature of these relationships in words. It is actually very helpful to be able to show what they would look like on a graph. Let's start with the tomatoes example. Have a look at the table below, which shows the prices of several different-sized bags of tomatoes.

Weight of bag (kilos)	Price (£)
1/4	
1/2	0.70
1	1.40
2	

Figure 8.1   Weight and price of tomatoes

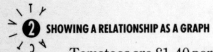

SHOWING A RELATIONSHIP AS A GRAPH

Tomatoes are £1.40 per kilo.

(a) Complete the two blanks in the table above and then plot the two missing points on the scatterplot below.
(b) How do you interpret the pattern of points on this graph?

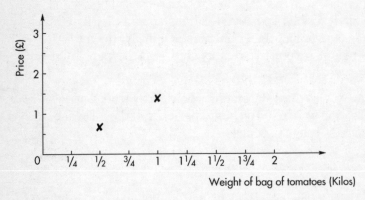

Figure 8.2   Scatterplot based on data from figure 8.1

As you can see from your graph, the points have a very particular pattern — they slope upwards to the right. Positive relationships always have this property. Expressed mathematically, the slope of the line joining the points is said to have a *positive gradient* — hence the term 'positive relationship'. This sort of clear pattern in the points on a scatterplot is also known as a *trend*. It is worth noting, however, that in the real world the relationship between the amount you buy of something and what you have to pay for it is slightly more complicated than this. Packages of things like breakfast cereal, washing powder, and so on, tend to work out cheaper if you buy in bulk. This sort of saving is sometimes known as 'the economies of scale' and can be described rather neatly as follows:

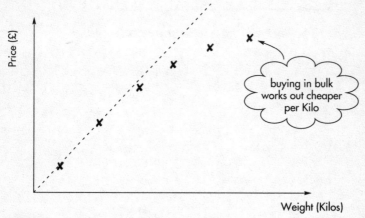

Figure 8.3   The economies of scale

Where there is a positive, there is usually a negative. You've probably already spotted that negative relationships slope downwards to the right and these have a *negative gradient*.

Negative relationships are sometimes described as *inverse* relationships.

The table and scatterplot in figures 8.4 and 8.5 overleaf show the negative relationship between the average July temperatures of eight cities and their longitude. Notice the 'negative' slope of the graph.

One feature of moving from describing a relationship in words to describing it graphically is that you need to think about how you are going to measure the variables in question. Measuring variables like price and weight is easy — there are accepted

City	Latitude (°)	Average maximum July temperature (°C)
Paris	48	24
Cairo	30	35
Ottawa	48	27
Oslo	60	23
Amsterdam	52	20
Madrid	40	30
Algiers	37	29
Moscow	56	24

Figure 8.4   The latitude and temperature of eight cities

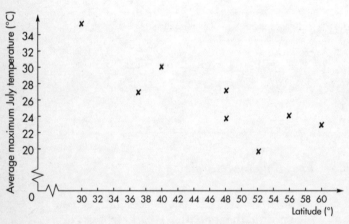

Figure 8.5   Scatterplot representing data given in figure 8.4

standard units for these (respectively, pence and kilograms would do). Similarly, leg length could be easily measured using centimetres. However, when it comes to measuring items like balloon size and the hardness of a pencil lead, the units of measure are not so obvious! Vague, wordy descriptions of relationships are fine for some situations, but if you wish or need to handle a relationship *statistically*, you will be involved in numbers and measurement. This brings its own problems of course; you will find that different people mean different things when they use the word 'size', for example.

Let's look now at the leg length/running speed example. You will remember that Carrie felt there should be a positive association between these two things — so, people with *longer* legs should be able to run *faster*. The following activity asks you to check out the truth of this for yourself.

③ SPEEDY LONG LEGS!

(a) Use the data below now to plot leg length against running time for the six children listed. (The point representing Nicola has been already plotted to get you started.)

(b) What does the graph suggest about the relationship which Carrie described?

Child's name	Leg length (cm)	Running time (s)
Nicola	80	23
Rashid	63	32
Gillian	75	23
Leroy	72	28
Wayne	75	25
Mandy	70	29

Figure 8.6   Leg length and running time

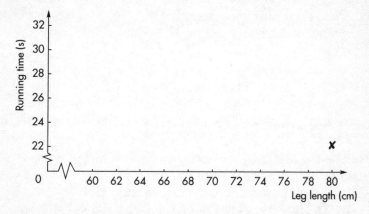

Figure 8.7   Scatterplot showing leg length against running time

● **COMMENTS**

Perhaps you were surprised that the general shape of the graph was sloping *downwards* to the right, rather than upwards? However, this is where you have to be very careful about the particular measure you use. Recording running time is a sensible way of measuring how fast someone can run, but you have to remember that the faster you run the shorter the time you take. So, running time is an inverse measure of running speed. Thus, although the graph has a negative slope, this shape does actually back up Carrie's claim that there is a positive association between leg length and running speed. However, this conclusion is only based on the evidence of the six children in the table. You would be sensible to reserve judgement on this relationship until further data were gathered!

 ④ REVISION!

To end this section, it would be a good idea to spend a few minutes reminding yourself about the main points we have covered.

(a) Think about the terms *positive* and *negative*, when applied to relationships, and what such relationships will look like on a graph.
(b) Try to think up some positive and negative relationships of your own and see if you can sketch their graphs.
(c) For each example you thought up in *(b)*, clarify for yourself exactly what is being measured, what the units of measure are and how the measurement might be carried out in a practical situation.

HOW STRONG IS YOUR RELATIONSHIP?

The aim of Section 1 was to help you get a clear picture of what is meant by a relationship between two things. In Section 2, you will build on that understanding to include the notion of correlation. The activity below is important, as it should help you to see what the basic idea of correlation is all about.

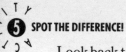

5 SPOT THE DIFFERENCE!

Look back to the two relationships covered in Section 1 and the graphs which they produced, that is:

(a) weight of tomatoes with price
(b) leg length with running speed.

Compare the two scatterplots and think about any differences you notice between their shape and pattern. Try to decide why they differ.

● **COMMENTS**

There are two key differences between these two graphs.

1   The tomatoes graph has a positive slope, whereas the leg length graph shows a negative trend.
2   In the tomatoes example all the points lie *exactly* on the line, whereas in the leg length example the points are scattered around the trend line.

The first point has already been discussed in the previous section. But the second point listed here captures the key issue of this section, and indeed the key issue of the whole chapter. In a sense, there is a 'perfect' relationship between the weight and price of tomatoes — the points which you plotted lie perfectly on the straight line. However, the scatter of the points in the second example suggests a more imperfect relationship. In particular, whereas a heavier bag of tomatoes will *always* cost more than a lighter one, it is not the case that someone with long legs will always be able to run faster than someone with short legs. All we can say is that, in general, there is a *tendency* for this to be true.

Statistical relationships are usually of this latter form. Unlike scientific or mathematical 'laws' or 'formulae' which describe 'perfect' relationships, statistical relationships can do no more than describe *trends*.

If the points plotted on the scatterplot form a very clear-cut pattern along a line, we call this showing *strong correlation* between the two things in question. If, however, there is a wide scatter of points, with only a faint trend, then the correlation is *weak*.

For example, this scatterplot shows a *strong positive correlation* between a person's arm length and their height:

Name	Arm length (cm)	Height (cm)
Tracey	73.5	169
Jayne	53	139
Darren	65	156
Michelle	58	144
Trudy	62	159
Scott	81	179

Figure 8.8   Height and arm length

Figure 8.9   Scatterplot showing height against arm length

On the other hand, the next scatterplot suggests a fairly *weak negative correlation*. The data were gathered from six children on the number of press-ups they could do in one minute and the length of their arms.

Person	Arm length (cm)	Number of press-ups (in 1 minute)
A	60	40
B	64	24
C	59	31
D	55	50
E	52	36
F	68	39

Figure 8.10   Press-ups and arm length

Figure 8.11   Scatterplot based on data from figure 8.10

Note that with a sample size of only six children it is difficult to draw any useful conclusions from these data. Furthermore, the number of press-ups which a person can do will increase greatly with practice. The number of press-ups recorded here seems fairly high, suggesting that this group of pupils had been in training for this statistical investigation!

6 REVISION

As a way of revising the key ideas in Section 2, try to think up four different relationships for each of the situations suggested under (a) to (d) below.

Strength of correlation	Type of relationship Positive	Negative
Strong	(a)	(b)
Weak	(c)	(d)

TESTING A RELATIONSHIP

In this section you will be asked to put these ideas of correlation into practice by investigating a particular relationship. As with previous chapters, you are reminded of the four PCAI stages of a statistical investigation. Here they are again:

P — Pose the question.
C — Collect the data.
A — Analyse the data.
I — Interpret the results.

7 'IT'S THE RICH WOT GETS THE PLEASURE . . .'

Spend a few minutes thinking about what different people earn and how they spend their money.

When you have identified a specific question that you would like to investigate (the 'P' stage of the cycle) think through how you might tackle the remaining three stages.

● **COMMENTS**

There are any number of interesting questions that you might have thought up. The question we shall pursue here will be to investigate the link between earnings and spending on food. As usual, the investigation will be written up using the PCAI structure.

Stage P

Our question is 'Do richer people tend to spend more on food?'

Stage C

If this activity were in the chapter on sampling, we might suggest that you stop 20 people in the street and ask them how much they earn and how much they spend on food.

However, there's a fair chance that the non-response rate would be extremely high! Before rushing out into the street with your questionnaire, it's always worth checking to see if someone hasn't already uncovered the information you need. And in this instance, they have! A useful source here is the most recent edition of the annual *Family Expenditure Survey*. The data shown in figure 8.12 below have been adapted from the 1986 edition.

Average gross weekly income (£)	Average weekly household expenditure (£)		
	Food	Alcohol	Tobacco
40	14.05	1.99	1.94
60	17.51	2.24	2.99
100	25.61	3.99	4.50
150	30.86	6.16	4.80
200	34.98	7.14	4.96
250	38.17	9.23	5.26
325	43.76	11.40	5.18
450	53.96	16.34	5.53
600	67.27	19.58	5.01

Source: Adopted from data in Department of Employment, *Family Expenditure Survey*, London, HMSO, 1986, pp 8–9

Figure 8.12   Expenditure of households at different levels of household income

The particular investigation we're looking at here is the relationship between earnings and spending on food. This puts the spotlight on the first two columns in the table.

Stage A

We're now ready to analyse the data, and a scatterplot seems to be the most useful tool for doing this.

ACTIVITY 8 PLOTTING AND PATTERN SPOTTING

(a) Plot the data from the first two columns of figure 8.12 above onto a scatterplot, as shown below.
(b) What does the scatterplot reveal about the relationship between earnings and spending on food?

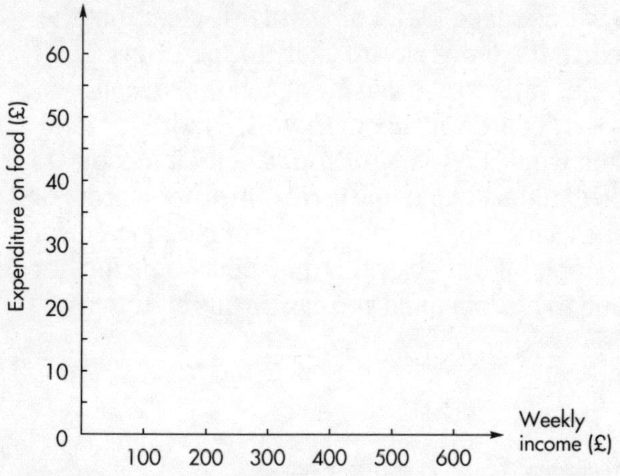

Figure 8.13 Scatterplot showing income and food expenditure

● COMMENTS

Stage I

You should have found that, as you might expect, the points on this graph do suggest an upward sloping trend to the right. In other words there is a positive relationship between how much people earn and how much they spend on food. But look a little closer at your graph and you will see that the underlying trend is not a straight line graph. The graph actually starts off quite steep and then becomes shallower as we move to the higher income groups on the right. Why do you think this is? The answer may not be immediately obvious, nor may you find it very easy to express your answer to this question in words. Spend a few minutes thinking about it now before reading on.

It is probably helpful to work your way across the graph, starting with £40 per week and, as you become richer, imagine how you might spend the extra money. Between £40 and £100, a large proportion of the extra money will go on more food for your family. This is why the graph is quite steep at that point.

However, when you're earning a lot of money, say £600 per week, your basic food needs are already met. You might spend some of the extra cash on a little lobster or caviar, but the chances are that you'll do something else with that money. So, the graph at this point is less steep.

Now you might be thinking that it is rather obvious that we have produced a graph of this shape. After all, it is fairly clear that the more money we earn, the more we are likely to spend on just about everything. So, rather than looking at *how much money* people spend on food at different income levels, a more interesting question would be *what proportion* of their income do they spend on food at different income levels. In other words, do richer people spend a larger or a smaller share of their income on food than poorer people? To answer this question, some further calculation will need to be done, and you can do this in Activity 9.

9 BIG SLICE, SMALL CAKE

Average weekly income (gross) (£)	Average amount spent on food (£)	Proportion of income spent on food (%)
40	14.05	35.1 (14.05/40 × 100)
65	17.51	
100	25.61	
150	30.86	
200	34.98	
250	38.17	
325	43.76	
450	53.96	
600	67.27	

Figure 8.14   Expenditure on food of households at different levels of household income

(a) Use your calculator to complete the table above by calculating the proportions of income spent on food for each weekly income level. (The first one has been done for you to get you started.)

(b) Plot your results in (a) on the scatterplot in figure 8.15. What interpretation would you make of this graph?

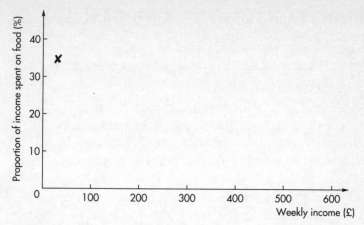

Figure 8.15   Scatterplot based on data in figure 8.14

● **COMMENTS**

The main point to notice from this second graph is that now the trend is downwards, not upwards. In other words, there is a negative relationship between earnings and the proportion of earnings spent on food. What this means in the real world is that richer people spend a smaller fraction of their earnings on food than poor people. One helpful way of picturing this is by comparing the two pie charts below.

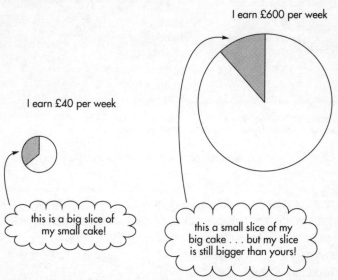

Figure 8.16   Pie charts showing comparison of relative amounts

RELATIONSHIPS CAN LEAD TO MISUNDERSTANDINGS

To end this chapter, we need to look at two important misunderstandings which often crop up when people try to interpret relationships.

The first of these is the point mentioned at the beginning of the chapter, and which is also referred to in the chapter title — the connection between 'cause' and 'correlation'. All should be revealed when you've had a go at Activity 10, so do it now.

⑩ THE CAUSES OF VIOLENT CRIME

The data given below show how the use of firearms in robberies has changed over recent years, and also how the percentage of men who smoke has changed over the same period.

Year	Robberies with firearms in England and Wales	% of men who smoke in UK
1977	1234	58
1978	996	55
1979	1038	55
1980	1149	55
1981	1893	50
1982	2560	49
1983	1957	47
1984	2098	47
1985	2539	46
1986	2651	45

Sources: Central Statistical Office *Social Trends 19*, London, HMSO, 1989, p. 183 and N. Wald et al., *UK Smoking Statistics*, Oxford, Oxford University Press, 1988, p. 23

Figure 8.17   Violent crime and the percentage of men who smoke

(a) How strong is the correlation between the percentage of men who smoke and the use of firearms during robberies over this period? (Don't bother to plot the data on a scatterplot, but you may find it helpful to imagine what they would look like if they were plotted.)

(b) What can you deduce from (a)?

● **COMMENTS**

It is clear that there seems to be a strong negative correlation between violent crime and male smoking. So what? Well, I suppose it is just *possible* that the money saved by smoking less has enabled hundreds of them finally to afford their own sawn-off shotguns and make a 'hit' on their local corner shops, but you will have to admit that any link between patterns in smoking and violent crime is unlikely.

The main point here is that, like many things, violent crime and smoking have both followed a steady trend over recent years. But to say that the change in one has *caused* the change in the other would be extremely rash! And this is what a *cause-and-effect* relationship means; that a reduction in the smoking habit among men actually caused violent crime to increase. Clearly this is nonsense. A strong correlation on its own is no proof of this cause-and-effect relationship. However, many people who should know better often assume it is. This misconception is a bit like unscrewing the oil warning light when it comes on in your car, on the grounds that, if there is no warning light, there is no problem!

The second common area of misconception to be explored here is concerned with the practice of *projection*. A projection means making an estimate of something in the future. After you've tried Activity 11, you will have a better idea about what this refers to.

11 LOOKING TOO FAR AHEAD

Year	Infant mortality (deaths per 1 000 live births)
1961	22.1
1971	19.7
1981	11.2
1985	9.4

Source: Central Statistical Office, *Social Trends 18*, London, HMSO, 1988, p. 116

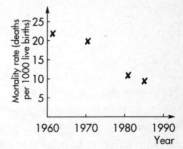

Figure 8.18   Infant mortality rates in the UK from 1961 to 1985

Figure 8.19   Scatterplot showing infant mortality rates in the UK from 1961 to 1985

The graph in figure 8.19 shows how the infant mortality rates have changed in the UK since 1960.

(a) How would you describe the general trend in mortality rates over the period?
(b) Use the graph to make a projection of the infant mortality rates in the year 2000.

● COMMENTS

The good news is that the graph clearly points to a steady decline in infant mortality rates over this 25-year period. Let's now project this trend into the future and see what the picture might be like around the year 2000. What you are being asked to do here is to project the graph beyond the range of data covered. If you draw a straight line through the points by eye, and then extend the line until the year 2000, you'll get something like the following:

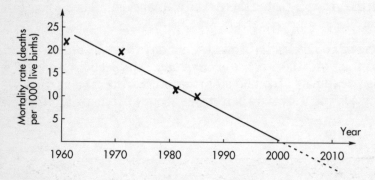

Figure 8.20   Projection of infant mortality rates to the year 2000

This projection seems to suggest that, by the year 2000, we will have entirely eliminated infant mortality! Well, it would be nice if we could, but this is clearly nonsense. Sadly, it isn't possible to imagine a time when we will ever eliminate infant mortality. The nonsense is made even clearer if we try to use this line to project beyond the year 2000. Are we to expect to have a *negative* infant mortality in the year 2010, for instance? Certainly not! So what has gone wrong, then? Well, we have actually made a number of dangerous assumptions here. First of all, we have put a straight line trend through the points on the graph. Straight lines are probably the easiest ones to draw, but they aren't always the most appropriate to describe the data on a graph. Secondly, we have assumed that this straight line trend will continue into the future. Well, given that the mortality rate can never fall below zero, this simply isn't possible. What is more likely is that the slope of the graph will gradually level off, although yet another possibility might be that it will start to increase again after reaching a certain level. (In fact the figures for 1986 showed a slightly higher rate of infant mortality than for 1985.) Finally, it is worth stressing that a trend cannot properly be deduced from plotting just four points. Trends can sometimes swing up and down in a regular cycle and this is simply not visible if too few points are plotted.

12 REVISION

Now to end this section, spend a few minutes thinking about the two main points it covered. Here they are again:

(a) A strong correlation doesn't prove a cause-and-effect relationship.
(b) It is a dangerous practice to project trends to far into the future. It is also unwise to assume a trend on the basis of only four or five pairs of values.

SUMMARY

An important type of investigation in Statistics is to explore the relationship between two variables. Normally this will involve collecting paired data and in this chapter we have plotted them on a scatterplot. The strength of the relationship between the two variables can be interpreted from the scatterplot. However, if you remember nothing else from this chapter, please do carry away the important point that a close correlation does not tell you anything about whether the relationship is a cause-and-effect one.

FOLLOW-UP EXERCISES

1   Investigate these data and try to find out more about the
    relationships they suggest.

   (a) A department store offered plastic Christmas trees at
       the following prices:

Height	Price (£)
2' 6"	11.50
5'	39.00
6'	59.00
7' 6"	99.00
8' 6"	125.00

Source: a large department store

Figure 8.21   Christmas trees by height and price

   (b) The data below give the masses and shoulder heights of
       various animals.

Name of animal	Mass (kg)	Shoulder height (cm)
Camel	450.000	230
Cat	2.500	18
Cheetah	21.000	77
Elephant	6600.000	320
Giraffe	1200.000	490
Hippopotamus	1700.000	145
Horse	650.000	175
Lion	100.000	100
Mouse	0.028	3
Rhinoceros	4064.000	175

Source: local zoo

Figure 8.22   Mass and shoulder height of various animals

   (c) The following data tell us the weight of a set of 5p coins.
       The coins were minted in different years but were all
       weighed on the same day in 1989.

Year	Weight of 5p coin (g)	Year	Weight of 5p coin (g)
1980	5.64	1971	6.67
1966	5.86	1977	5.69
1975	5.65	1953	5.63
1978	5.73	1967	5.59
1957	5.60	1963	5.60
1951	5.62	1964	5.74
1955	5.61	1956	5.67
1970	5.55	1979	5.67

Source: study in local school

Figure 8.23 Weight and year of 5p coins

2 Figure 8.24 below gives the top second-hand prices on two cars year by year.

Car make	Price of new car (£)	Price of car (£) aged:						
		1 yr	2 yr	3 yr	4 yr	5 yr	6 yr	7 yr
Ford Fiesta Popular 1.0 (Mar '89)	5299	4250	3800	3275	2775	2400	2125	1750
Vauxhall Cavalier 1.6	8720	6500	5750	4625	3850	3100	2475	1900

Figure 8.24 Age and price of two cars

(a) For each car, calculate these second-hand prices as a percentage of the price for a new car.

(b) Plot the two sets of percentage figures against age of car onto the same graph. What does your graph reveal about the depreciation of each car?

9 The Seamy Side of Statistics

In this chapter we look at some of the common misuses of statistics. Sometimes these occur quite innocently, but, especially where advertisers are involved, the aim can be deliberately to mislead. In the space available here we are just able to touch on three fertile areas of distortion — averages, percentages and graphs.

Key terms: *average, mode, median, mean, percentage.*

ABUSING AVERAGES

Before listing some of the ways in which averages are often misused and abused, it's worth making the point that averages are extremely useful calculations to carry out. The main purpose of an average is to give an idea of the sort of typical values you can expect from whatever you are interested in. Once you know the average, you are then in a position to make useful comparisons.

For example, let's investigate whether there is any truth in the suggestion that Britain is a very dirty country. Having 'posed' the question ('Is Britain a dirty country?'), the next stage of the PCAI cycle is to 'collect' relevant data. We might start by looking at litter as a measure of how dirty Britain is, but things like the amount of litter that is left lying around are hard to measure accurately. However there are official figures on how much acid rain and air pollution we produce. Air pollution is usually measured in terms of the number of tonnes of sulphur dioxide emitted in the course of a year. It has been calculated that, in 1985, the air pollution of sulphur dioxide emitted by the UK was 3.5 million tonnes (Source: Central Statistical Office, *Social Trends 19*, London, HMSO , 1988, p. 157). Now, it is very hard to know how to respond to this information — we have no idea whether this is a lot of pollution or a little. A useful comparison would be with the typical levels of pollution in neighbouring countries. Calculating the average levels of sulphur dioxide emissions from the other 11 European Community (EC) partners, we get a figure of 1.15 million tonnes for the same year. So clearly Britain is well on the wrong side of this particular average. Here are the figures in full:

Country	Pollution (million tonnes)	Country	Pollution (million tonnes)
United Kingdom	3.50	Irish Republic	0.10
Belgium	0.60	Italy	3.20
Denmark	0.30	Luxembourg	0.02
France	1.70	Netherlands	0.20
Germany	2.60	Portugal	0.30
Greece	0.70	Spain	2.90

Definitions and methods of measurement may differ from country to country

Source: Central Statistical Office, *Social Trends 19*, London, HMSO, 1988, p. 157

Figure 9.1   Air pollution—sulphur dioxide emissions: EC comparison 1985

① THE DUSTBIN OF EUROPE

Read carefully through the data above and try to decide whether you agree with the statement that Britain is the 'dustbin of Europe'.

● COMMENTS

It is clear that the UK not only has an above average level of air pollution, but also has the highest actual level of pollution of all her European partners. Or does she? Well, a shrewd politician who wanted to defend Britain's record on pollution might respond to figure 9.1 by saying the following:

> It simply isn't true to say that Britain is a high polluter. Firstly, as you can see from the footnote below the table, because of different definitions and methods of measurement between the countries concerned, it isn't possible to make comparisons. Secondly, it isn't surprising that Britain has one of the highest levels of pollution, since

we have one of the highest populations. It just doesn't make sense to compare our pollution levels with the *average* levels of European countries when this figure includes tiny countries like Luxembourg. You aren't comparing like with like.

The next exercise asks you to respond to this second point of whether this average provides a fair comparison.

2 COMPARING LIKE WITH LIKE

Given below are the populations of the 12 countries in the EC. Try to find a way of using this additional information to make a fairer comparison between Britain's levels of air pollution and those of her European partners.

Country	Population (millions)	Country	Population (millions)
United Kingdom	56.8	Irish Republic	3.5
Belgium	9.9	Italy	57.2
Denmark	5.1	Luxembourg	0.4
France	55.4	Netherlands	14.6
Germany	61.1	Portugal	10.2
Greece	10.0	Spain	38.6

Source: Central Statistical Office, *Social Trends 19*, London, HMSO, 1988, p. 34

Figure 9.2   Population of EC countries, 1986

● COMMENTS

Perhaps a fairer comparison would be to calculate the average amount of sulphur dioxide emitted *per person* for each country. So, for example, there are 3.50 million tonnes emitted in the UK, which has a population of 56.8 million people. Dividing the first figure by the second, we get the average emission per person, which comes to roughly 0.061 tonnes. Figure 9.3 gives the corresponding figures for all 12 countries. You might like to check these figures before reading on, just to make sure you follow how they were calculated.

Country	Pollution (tonnes)	Country	Pollution (tonnes)
United Kingdom	0.06	Irish Republic	0.03
Belgium	0.06	Italy	0.06
Denmark	0.06	Luxembourg	0.05
France	0.03	Netherlands	0.01
Germany	0.04	Portugal	0.03
Greece	0.07	Spain	0.08

Figure 9.3   Average pollution per head of population for EC countries

So, based on these figures, Britain's record doesn't look quite so bad. Rather than being the worst polluter overall, she can claim to be merely 'one of the worst polluters per head'. However, it may be of small consolation to us that Britain isn't as bad as, say, Greece, in this respect, bearing in mind that Greece produces such low levels of pollution overall.

We end this section on averages with a number of examples of situations where averages are commonly misused.

❸ AVOIDING AVERAGES

Read through the following statements and try to say exactly what is wrong with them.

(a) I come from an average family with 2.4 children.

(b) This school is really dreadful — half the pupils are below average!

(c) On the outward journey we averaged 60 mile/h and on the return journey we averaged 30 mile/h, so, overall, our average speed was 45 mile/h.

(d) The air temperatures at midday, measured in degrees Celsius, each day over a week were: 19, 22, 21, 20, 18, 19, 22. This means that the average temperature was:

$$(19+22+21+20+18+19+22) \div 7 = 20.142857°C$$

● COMMENTS

(a) Although the average number of children in a family is around 2.4, it must be remembered that this is the mean value which is impossible to achieve for any particular family. The mode or the median would be a more appropriate average here, as these would produce a whole number answer (say 2 or 3 children per family).

(b) The phrase 'below average' is often taken to mean 'inferior' or 'unacceptably low'. In fact, if we take this average to refer to the median value of the distribution, then you would expect that half the values would be below the average and half would be above it. So this school hasn't done so badly — in fact it is just about average!

(c) Something to be wary of is taking means of speeds — it simply doesn't work out, except in very artificial cases. The easiest way to convince yourself of this is to work out the total time taken for both journeys. For example, suppose that in this case the return journey is 120 miles — 60 miles out and 60 miles back. Then the total time taken for both stages of the journey is 3 hours (1 hour out and 2 hours back). 120 miles covered in 3 hours means an average of 40 mile/h, not 45 mile/h as stated.

(d) It is quite alright to calculate the mean in this example, but even though the calculator gives an answer to eight figures of accuracy, it is silly to give this as your answer. As you can see from the original temperatures, they were clearly measured accurate to the nearest whole number of degrees, so the average should be rounded to the roughly same level of accuracy — in this case the answer 20 or 20.1 degrees Celsius would be appropriate.

PRETENDING WITH PERCENTAGES

Of all the areas where people misuse statistics, misleading information wrapped up in percentages is one of the most common. In fact, did you know that 92% of misleading statistics are based on percentages? You didn't? Well, that's not surprising, because I just made that figure up out of my head! It is remarkable just how many people do make up 'statistical facts' out of their head and get away with it. Particularly when the information is expressed as a percentage, most people tend to believe facts and figures simply because they look impressive. For example, in an advertisement for a domestic fire protection kit, the following claim was made:

Fact—80% of fire engines called out in the UK are for domestic fires . . .

Since most of us have no idea what the expected percentage would be, this claim seems reasonable. (Clearly the advertiser wished us to take the threat of domestic fires more seriously.) But when checked against Home Office data, the actual figure turns out to be only 10%!

Often, incorrect claims based on percentages are unwittingly made. For example, the newspaper headline which claimed that '50% of people drive on faulty brakes' was based on the (correct) information that, of the 10 million cars that had failed their MOT test over the previous two years, over half had faulty brakes.

4 'BRAKING' THE RULES OF LOGIC

Think about the newspaper headline above. Using the statistical ideas already covered in this book, indicate why the logic is at fault.

● COMMENTS

The claim is based on an admittedly large sample of cars tested (10 million!). However, by its nature, the sample is extremely biased. First, only cars which are three years or older are required to take an MOT test. Second, of these older cars, only those which failed the test were included in the sample. For these two reasons, then, the sample chosen is much more likely to contain cars with faulty brakes than the total population of all cars on the roads. The point is made even more clearly if we look at the chart shown in figure 9.4 overleaf (impression only, and not based on real data).

Note that the different proportions of motorists are represented by different areas of this chart. The shaded part of the chart represents those new cars for which no MOT test is required. The portion of the remainder of the graph which is dotted represents those cars which were tested and failed. The sample on which the headline was based was taken only from this dotted portion, but the conclusions were applied to the complete graph.

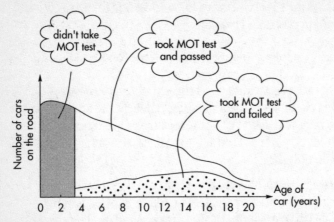

Figure 9.4   Impression graph showing cars which have taken the MOT test

This last example showed how a percentage may be used incorrectly. Let's now turn to an example where a percentage should have been used, but wasn't.

5 ANYONE CAN GET AN 'A' IN MATHS!

What do the following data tell you about how easy or difficult Maths, Physics and Classical Studies are at GCSE level?

Subject	Number of grade 'A' passes
Mathematics	38 570
Physics	22 450
Classical Studies	8 550

Source: *Times Educational Supplement*, 3rd February, 1989, p. A4

Figure 9.5   The number of grade 'A' passes in GCSE, 1988

● COMMENTS

On their own, the data shown in figure 9.5 actually tell us very little about how hard it is to get a grade 'A' in these subjects at GCSE level. The figures are meaningless without taking into account how many students actually sat the three exams. In fact there was a big difference in these numbers — there were 653 716 students who sat the Maths exam, 244 025 who sat Physics and only 22 316 who sat Classical Studies. With this added information you can go on to calculate the proportion of grade 'A' passes for each subject; this is shown below, expressed as a percentage in the final column of the table. Check these figures yourself now before reading on.

Subject	Number of grade 'A' passes	Number examined	Percentage grade 'A'
Mathematics	38 570	653 716	5.9
Physics	22 450	244 025	9.2
Classical Studies	8 550	22 316	38.3

Source: *Times Educational Supplement*, 3rd February, 1989, p. A4

Figure 9.6   The percentage of grade 'A' passes in GCSE, 1988

So, when the percentage number of passes is calculated, a very different picture results. As you can see from the table, out of every 100 candidates examined in each of these examinations, a grade 'A' was awarded to roughly 6 in Mathematics, 9 in Physics, and 38 in Classical Studies. On this evidence it would seem that Mathematics is actually the *hardest* of the three. Of course, even this is something of a simplification. It could be, for example, that, overall, the small number of students entered for Classical Studies are brighter or better taught than average, and it is for this reason that there is such a very high proportion of grade 'A' passes in this subject. However, without knowing more about the students entered for these examinations, we really just cannot say!

CHEATING WITH CHARTS

Of the many ways available that can be used to mislead people with Statistics, perhaps the most popular is the misuse of graphs and charts. This is one of the most creative and imaginative fields open to advertisers who wish to entice the consumer to buy their product, and lack of space prevents us from doing it full justice here! The main feature of a successful cheating chart is that it should leave the punter feeling what the advertiser wants him or her to feel, whatever the details of the graph actually say. Generally, people read graphs in much the same way that they read newspapers — they simply scan the main features (the headlines) and don't spend a great deal of time checking out the fine print.

6 FIRST IMPRESSIONS

Have a quick look at this graph and make a note about the main thing that you think it shows.

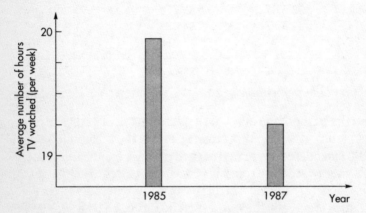

Source: Central Statistical Office, *Social Trends 19*, London, HMSO, 1989, p. 163

Figure 9.7   Children's (aged 4–15) TV viewing habits

● COMMENTS

The most obvious feature of this graph is that it shows a dramatic drop in TV viewing by children in the 4–15 year age range between 1985 and 1987. In fact, the number of hours viewed seems to have dropped to about *one quarter* of what they were two years before. This would indeed be amazing — if it were true — which, of course, it isn't! Have a look at the vertical axis of the graph. From this you can read off that the average number of hours viewed dropped over the two-year period from about 20 hours to about 19¼ hours. (The actual figures are 19 hours 59 minutes in 1985 and 19 hours 14 minutes in 1987.) You might like to pause for a few moments before reading on and think about how this misleading impression has been achieved.

This is what is sometimes known in the USA as a 'gee-whizz' graph, for the obvious reason that you take one look at how steep the slope is and say, 'gee-whizz!'. But let's now redraw the graph in a slightly different way. The graph below shows the same information but presented in a more honest and less dramatic way. Compare the two graphs and spend a few moments thinking about why figures 9.7 and 9.8 have different shapes.

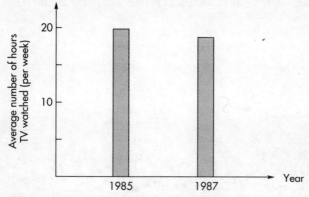

Figure 9.8   Improved version of figure 9.7

So, the two graphs have very different shapes because the scales on the vertical axis are different. For the first graph, the vertical scale runs from 19 hours to 20 hours. Because this covers such a narrow range, any change seems greatly magnified. A much more realistic impression is given with the second graph which allows you to see how big the change was in relation to the actual starting value of zero hours.

⑦ GRAPHS WHICH DON'T START AT ZERO

Try to think of one advantage and one disadvantage of drawing a graph like the first of the two above, where the vertical scale doesn't start at zero.

● COMMENTS

I've already indicated the main disadvantage of drawing a graph which doesn't start at zero — it can make any changes appear much greater than they actually are and so create a false impression. The other side of this coin is that, sometimes, you want to display a set of data which contain only fairly small changes. For example, have a look at the data in figure 9.9.

Year	1984	1985	1986	1987
Marriages	396 000	393 000	394 000	398 000

Source: Central Statistical Office, *Social Trends 19*, London, HMSO, 1988, p. 41

Figure 9.9   The number of marriages in the UK from 1984 to 1987

Now let's see what these data would look like if plotted in the usual way.

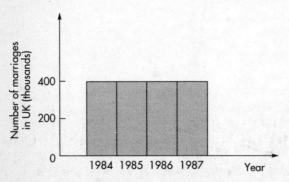

Figure 9.10   Graph showing the number of marriages in the UK between 1984 and 1987

Clearly this graph isn't very helpful — by starting the vertical scale at zero, all we get is a horizontal straight line graph which fails to reveal any other patterns in the data. However, if you do wish to explore these small changes over time, a graph which starts at, say, 390 000 would be more helpful — thus:

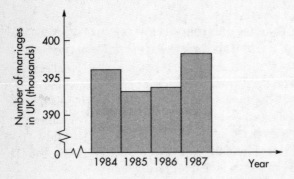

Figure 9.11   Figure 9.10 redrawn with the origin not at zero

Notice that the fact that the vertical scale does not start at zero is indicated by the break on the axis as shown below.

Now let's turn to another common type of misleading graph. Have a look at the graph below and then answer the question in Activity 8.

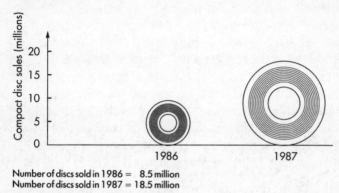

Number of discs sold in 1986 =   8.5 million
Number of discs sold in 1987 = 18.5 million

Source: Central Statistical Office, *Social Trends 19*, London, HMSO, 1988, p. 165

Figure 9.12   Sale of compact discs

8 IN THE CHARTS

In what way do you think this graph gives a misleading impression of the data?

● COMMENTS

I've drawn this graph to show up a favourite trick of advertisers which is, once again, to make differences appear to be bigger than they actually are. First of all, look at the chart and try to decide how many times bigger the large disc is than the smaller one. You probably would say that it was five or six times as big (comparing areas). But when you look at the data shown below the graph, the 1987 sales were actually about two to three times bigger than in 1986. Now, although the second disc is two and a half times taller than the first disc, it is also two and a half times wider. As a casual observer, you will probably base your impression on the difference between the two discs by comparing their *areas* and not their *heights*. And, although the correct data are included on the graph, it is the visual *impression* that most people tend to come away with when they look at these sorts of charts that counts.

SUMMARY

This chapter has concentrated on three important statistical ideas which are often the basis for misleading information — averages, percentages and graphs. Probably the main reason for confusion in these areas is that people don't all share the same understanding of what the terms mean. For example, in some West Indian dialects, 'to average' means 'to estimate'. Percentages are not generally understood and are commonly avoided by most people, which therefore leaves them vulnerable to impressive-sounding statistics. Finally, there are many ways in which graphs can be redrawn so as to give the reader a quite different impression of the key features of the data.

Finally, I hope that the ideas contained in this book have given you some notion of the key issues of Statistics and that you feel better equipped to defend yourself when someone tries to blind you with facts and figures.

FOLLOW-UP EXERCISES

1   Half the students taking a particular examination will get below average marks. Which average is being referred to here and do you agree that the statement is true?

2

	Women under 65	Women 75 and over
Death from lung cancer	2 981	3 299
Total deaths to women in these age groups	25 302	102 946

Source: N. Wells, *Women's Health Today*, London, Office of Health Economics, 1987, p. 27

Figure 9.13   Lung cancer deaths among women by age

Fact: lung cancer kills more women aged over 75 than women aged under 65. This statement is based on the statistics given in figure 9.13.

Do you agree with the interpretation of these figures given above? (Note that if you are unhappy with the interpretation, try calculating lung cancer deaths as a percentage of the total for each age group.)

3   The graph below shows the dramatic decline in membership of the Anglican church between 1975 and 1987.

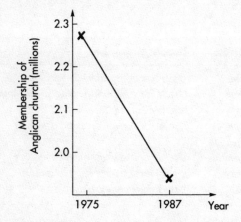

Figure 9.14   Membership of the Anglican church, 1975 to 1987

This graph is misleading in two ways. What are they?
Redraw the graph to give a fairer picture of the data.

Answers to Follow-up Exercises

CHAPTER 1

1

Graph or diagram	Type of data	Examples of conclusions
Bar chart	Discrete	Useful for comparing categories
Pie chart	Discrete	Useful for comparing categories within the same group
Stemplot	Discrete or continuous	Useful for showing spread of values
Histogram	Continuous	Useful for showing spread of values
Scatterplot	Paired	Useful for showing the relationship between two variables

2 Some justifications for learning Statistics:

(a) Statistics crop up in a variety of different fields such as social science, science, and so on.

(b) Statistics provides a way of understanding patterns in data.

(c) An understanding of Statistics is the best defence against being blinded by facts and figures.

3 The two bags of crisps will not be of exactly the same weight. As for any production process, there will be variation in the weights of each of the bags of crisps. (This is called natural variation.) In fact, no two things can ever weigh *exactly* the same because finer grades of weighing accuracy will eventually show up differences in their weight.

4   The four stages of a statistical investigation are:

P — Pose the question.
C — Collect the data.
A — Analyse the data.
I   — Interpret the results.

The four questions match up to these stages as follows:
P=(d), C=(c), A=(a) and I=(b).

CHAPTER 2

1   Suppose you posed the following question: 'Have house
    prices in your town risen more quickly over the last year than
    over the previous year?'.

    The nine questions in the checklist would look something like
    the following:

    (i) The problem has been fairly clearly posed in your
        question.
    (ii) Average price rises over the last 12 months and the
        12 months before this.
    (iii) Thousands of pounds.
    (iv) There are several possible sources of data including
        local estate agents and back copies of the local
        newspaper.
    (v) House prices this month (year 2), twelve months ago
        (year 1) and twelve months before that (year 0).
    (vi) Calculate price increases between year 0 and year 1
        and year 1 and year 2 for a range of different types of
        houses, and then compare their averages.
    (vii) Problems include how many houses and what type of
        houses to sample and whether price increases should
        be calculated in money or percentage terms.
    (viii) Yes.
    (ix) The answer to this question depends on why you
        embarked on the investigation in the first place. It
        could be, for example, that your findings would help
        you to decide on the best time to buy a home and
        whether, in your town at this time, a terraced or
        semi-detached house is better value for money.

2 Primary data are data you collect yourself (perhaps through an experiment or survey). Secondary data are usually obtained from books, magazines, and official and unofficial records, and are drawn from someone else's findings.

(a) primary   (c) secondary
(b) primary   (d) primary

3 A category is a type of measure which has a name rather than a number. Variables, on the other hand, are numbers. Examples of a *category* include tree type (ash, oak, yew, . . .) and nationality (British, French, . . .). Examples of a variable include length, time, GNP, etc.

4 Discrete and continuous variables are both based on numbers. They differ in that a discrete variable is restricted in the number of values that it can take. (For example, shoe size, score in darts, money). Continuous variables, on the other hand, are not restricted in this way and the number of values that they can take are theoretically infinite. In practice, however, even continuous variables are restricted within the accuracy of measurement. For example, most of us would find it difficult to measure a person's height more accurately than to the nearest centimetre. This means that there are only a limited number of heights that a person can be. Thus continuous variables (like height, time, temperature) often, in practice, become treated like discrete variables.

5 What categories and discrete variables share is that they are both discrete. This is important when it comes to choosing a suitable graph to represent them.

CHAPTER 3

1 Bar charts and pie charts are suitable for portraying data from types (a) and (b) but not type (c).

2 The gaps between the bars of a bar chart help to emphasise the fact that the data being represented are *discrete*.

3 Carbon dioxide 49%, methane 18%, CFCs 14%, nitrous oxide 6%, other 13%.

4 **(a)** The main features are as follows:
  (i) For both years, ILR was the most popular.
  (ii) Very few people listened to Radio 3!
 (iii) The patterns for both years are roughly similar.

   (b) Although the ILR bar is the tallest, it represents a large number of different independent local radio stations. Thus, Radio 1 is the most listened to *single* radio station in the UK.

   (c) Pie charts showing the share of all listening by radio station.

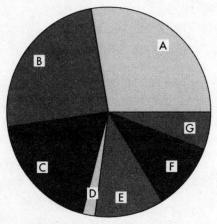

A ILR
B Radio 1
C Radio 2
D Radio 3
E Radio 4
F BBC local
G others

Source: *The Independent,* 26th April, 1989, p. 17

Figure A.1   Radio listening, 1987

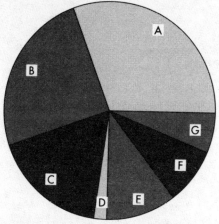

A ILR
B Radio 1
C Radio 2
D Radio 3
E Radio 4
F BBC local
G others

Source: *The Independent,* 26th April, 1989, p. 17

Figure A.2   Radio listening, 1988

5   A bar chart would be more suitable to represent these data
    because they are category data and therefore discrete. A pie
    chart would not be suitable because, taken together, the
    collective ages of the five people do not mean anything
    sensible.

CHAPTER 4

1

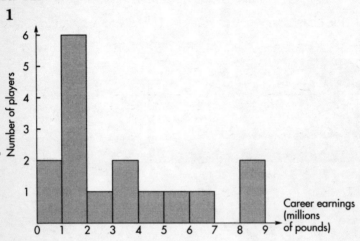

Source: data compiled from various sources

*Figure A.3   Histogram of career earnings of the top men and
women seeds at Wimbledon, 1989*

2

Women's heights N = 8	H = 190	Men's heights N = 8
—	19	—00
8—	18	—888
3—	18	—033
5—	17	—
330—	17	—
5—	16	—

1 Outliers
L = 165
(Each interval 5, 18—0 is 180 cm)

*Figure A.4   Back-to-back stemplot showing the heights of tennis
players*

3

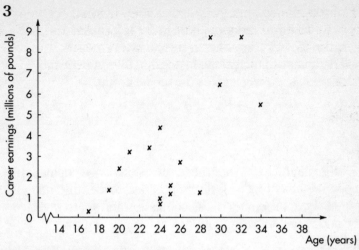

Source: data compiled from various sources

Figure A.5   Scatterplot showing age and earnings of 16 tennis players

CHAPTER 5

1   **(a)** You would expect the histogram to have a central peak and tails on either side, as follows:

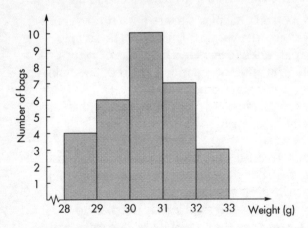

Source: data compiled from various sources

Figure A.6   Histogram showing the weights of 30 bags of crisps

(b) The reason for this shape is that you would expect there to be a natural variation, both in the bag-filling process and in the accuracy of your own measurements.

(c) The tallest column of the histogram tells you the mode (strictly speaking it gives the modal group).

2 **(a)** (ii)   **(b)** (i)   **(c)** (ii)   **(d)** (ii)

CHAPTER 6

1 It is often useful to find out the features of a large population (of people, objects, etc.). It is impractical to identify and examine every member of the population and so, to save time and expense, we simply look at a representative sample.

2 The key characteristic of a good sample is that it is *representative* of the population from which it has been taken.

3 You can never ensure that your sample perfectly reflects the characteristics of the population from which it is taken (unless you sample the entire population). However, here are the main ways of ensuring that your sample is as representative as possible:

- Choose a reasonably large sample.
- Adopt a method of selection which avoids sampling bias.

4 **(a)** The workmen on a building site are not a representative cross-section of the voting population. The sample should be extended to include a full range of voters: women, men in other occupations, retired, unemployed and disabled men and women etc.

(b) It is likely that women will outnumber men in this sample and that employed women will also be under-represented.

(c) The takings for most shops are generally higher on Saturdays than on other days of the week. Also, there are likely to be seasonal patterns (such as Christmas) which this twelve-week sample may not pick up.

(d) Both the pattern and the cost of telephone calls vary throughout the day and between weekdays and weekends.

CHAPTER 7

1   In order to decide on differences between two samples, (i) and (iv) would be most useful.

2   **(a)** The birth weights of a sample of babies born to mothers who smoked during pregnancy and the birth weights of a matched sample of babies born to non-smoking mothers.
    (b) The data could be usefully represented either on a back-to-back stemplot or on two separate histograms.

3   You need to think about the following questions:

    ● How big is the actual difference between the two groups (probably based on comparing the two averages)?
    ● How much variation is there within in each of the groups?
    ● How large are the sample sizes in each group?
    ● How significant is the difference between the averages, bearing in mind your answers to the above questions?

CHAPTER 8

1   **(a)** The data from figure 8.21 when graphed on a scatterplot look like the following:

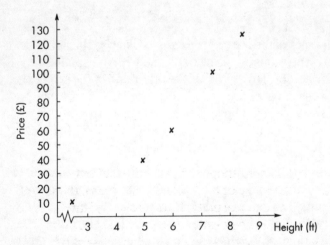

Figure A.7   Scatterplot showing height and price of Christmas trees

The general trend of these points shows a clear positive association between the height of a tree and its price. However, if you look closely at the pattern that the points make, the trend is not linear (a straight line) but curves upwards. You might like to speculate why this is.

(b)

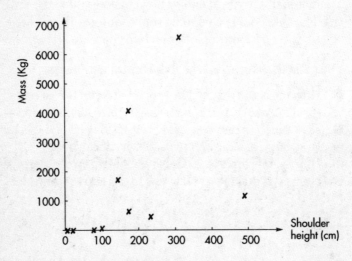

Figure A.8   Scatterplot showing mass and sholder height of 10 different animals

These points make a curious pattern. Clearly, the lightest animal — the mouse — is also the one with the smallest shoulder height. However, at the other end of the scale, the two points representing the elephant and the giraffe are widely contrasting. These data also raise interesting questions of measurement. For example, it isn't obvious where exactly a giraffe's shoulder begins — or ends!

(c)   There is no obvious pattern in the points shown in figure A.9 and the scatterplot seems to suggest that coins get neither significantly heavier over time (due to grime), nor significantly lighter over time (due to wear). The one maverick point, the coin weighing 6.67 g was discovered afterwards to have a blob of chewing-gum stuck to the reverse side!

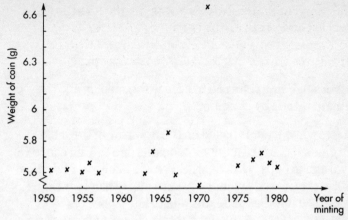

Figure A.9   Scatterplot showing weight of 5p coins against year of minting

2 (a)

Car make	Price of new car (%)	Price of car (as a % of new price) aged:						
		1 yr	2 yr	3 yr	4 yr	5 yr	6 yr	7 yr
Ford Fiesta Popular 1.0	100	80	72	62	52	45	40	33
Vauxhall Cavalier	100	75	66	53	44	36	28	22

Figure A.10   Prices of second-hand cars as a percentage of prices new, March 1989

(b)

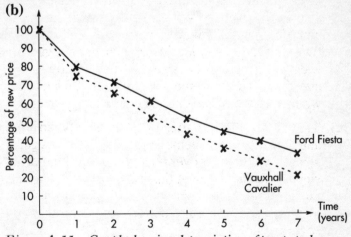

Figure A.11   Graph showing depreciation of two popular cars

The graphs suggest that, relatively speaking, the Fiesta holds its value better than the Cavalier.

CHAPTER 9

1 The average being referred to here is the median and the statement is true by definition.

2 The fact, while true, is based on the first row of the table which gives the actual number of deaths due to lung cancer in the two age groups. However, there are many more deaths in total in the 75-and-over age group (more than four times as many). If the number of deaths due to lung cancer is calculated as a *percentage* of the total number of deaths in each age group, a rather different picture emerges. In fact, lung cancer accounts for 11.8% of all deaths among women aged under 65, but only 3.2% of deaths among women aged 75 and over.

3 The graph is misleading in the following two ways:

● The origin does not start at zero which exaggerates the extent of the decline in church membership.
● The scale on the horizontal axis is much too small. This accentuates the effect of the origin not starting at zero.

Further Reading

Here is a basic list of readable source books containing interesting data for use in a statistical investigation.

Central Statistical Office, *Annual Abstract of Statistics*, London, HMSO, 1989*

Central Statistical Office, *Key Data*, London, HMSO, 1988*

Central Statistical Office, *Regional Trends 23*, London, HMSO, 1988 *

Central Statistical Office, *Social Trends*, London, HMSO, 1989*

Department of Education and Science, *Young People in the Eighties*, London, HMSO, 1983

Department of Employment, *Family Expenditure Survey 1986*, London, HMSO, 1988*

Equal Opportunities Commission, *Women and Men in Britain: A Research Profile*, London, HMSO, 1988*

M. S. Hoffman, *The World Almanac and Book of Facts*, London, Pharos Books, 1989

R. Jowell, S. Witherspoon and L. Brooks, *British Social Attitudes: the 5th Report*, Aldershot, Gower, 1988*

N. McWhirter (ed.), *Guinness Books of Answers*, Enfield, Guinness Superlatives Ltd, 1988*

N. McWhirter (ed.), *Guinness Books of Records*, Enfield, Guinness Superlatives Ltd, 1988*

Office of Population Censuses and Surveys, *General Household Survey 1986*, London, HMSO, 1989*

P. Scaping (ed.), *BPI Year Book 1989*, London, British Phonographic Industry Limited, 1989*

Whitaker's Almanack, London, J. Whitaker and Sons Ltd., 1989*

*These publications are produced annually or on a regular basis. Look out for the most recent edition.

Here are some suggestions for reading which will take you further and deeper into the world of statistical analysis.

J. Bell, *Doing Your Own Research Project*, Milton Keynes, Open University Press, 1987

M. Chapman and B. Mahon, *Plain Figures*, London, HMSO, 1986

A. Graham, *Statistical Investigations in the Secondary School*, Cambridge, Cambridge University Press, 1987

D. Huff, *How to Lie with Statistics*, Harmondsworth, Penguin Books, 1973

D. Huff, *How to Take a Chance*, Harmondsworth, Penguin Books, 1978

C. Marsh, *Exploring Data: An Introduction to Data Analysis for Social Scientists*, London, Polity Press, 1988

S. Reid, *Working with Statistics: An Introduction to Quantitative Methods for Social Scientists*, London, Polity Press, 1987

Glossary

ALTERNATIVE HYPOTHESIS
See NULL HYPOTHESIS.

BIAS
This means unfairly favouring one thing at the expense of
another — commonly met in sampling when the sample that has
been chosen doesn't fairly reflect the features of the total
population from which it has been taken.

BLIND TRIAL
A problem which an experimenter faces when trying things out
on humans is that they sometimes show a response in the trial
simply because they feel they are expected to. A way of avoiding
this is for the experimenter not to reveal to the participants
which of two groups they are in — the experimental group or
the control group. This approach is called a *blind trial* — i.e. the
participants are 'blind'.

CATEGORICAL DATA
Often data are collected as numbers, but sometimes we wish to
count the number of times certain categories of things occur (for
example, four calling birds, three French hens, etc.!). For
obvious reasons, this sort of data based on categories are called
categorical data.

CAUSAL RELATIONSHIPS
Many things can be shown to have a statistical relationship with
each other and this usually shows up when the relevant data are
graphed. Only some of these statistical relationships will be
causal — i.e. relationships where changes in one of the things
you are looking at actually *cause* the change in the other. For
example, there is a causal relationship between how much
people earn and what they spend.

COEFFICIENT OF CORRELATION
Correlation is how we describe the strength of the connection
between things. For example, there is a strong correlation

between a person's height and their shoe size. *The correlation coefficient* (usually given as a number between −1 and 1) is a way of measuring this strength of connection.

CONFIDENCE INTERVAL
A 95% *confidence interval* is a range of values between which a person could feel 95% confident that the true value of something lies. See INTERVAL ESTIMATE.

CONTROL GROUP
It is said that, with proper treatment, 'flu' will last seven days, but left untreated it will drag on for a week! The point here is that you can't really say how successful your treatment has been unless you can compare the results with what would happen if you didn't take any treatment. In experiments where things like new drugs are being tested, it is therefore necessary to use two groups of patients — the *experimental* group who are given the drug, and a similar sample of people called the *control* group who are given no treatment. (However, see also PLACEBO EFFECT.) The drug will only be successful if the experimental group do noticeably better than the control group and have no serious side-effects.

CROSS-SECTIONAL DATA
There are some experiments, such as investigating the effects of smoking on people's health, for example, where data are collected on the same group of people over many months or years. Data collected in this way are called *longitudinal data*. *Cross-sectional data*, on the other hand, are collected at just one point in time.

DOUBLE-BLIND TRIAL
A *double-blind trial* is where both the participants and the experimenter are kept in the dark as to which people were allocated to the experimental group and which to the control group. See BLIND TRIAL.

EXPERIMENTAL GROUP
See CONTROL GROUP.

INDEPENDENT VARIABLE
If two variables are linked and you feel confident that there is a causal relationship between them, then the variable which does

the causing is called the *independent* variable and the other one is called the *dependent* variable.

INDEX NUMBER
Usually in Statistics we collect data by measuring things directly. However, sometimes this is hard to do, or it may produce numbers which are difficult to handle and compare. If this is the case, a new scale of measure is used — called an *index number*. A good example of this is the Retail Price Index (RPI) which is a measure of inflation that takes account of the price increases of many different goods.

INTERVAL ESTIMATE
Often when we have to make an estimate of some value we come up with a single figure — known as a *point estimate*. In Statistics an alternative is to indicate the range of values that the true value is likely to take, and this range is called an *interval estimate*. You could go further and state that you are, say, 95% confident that the value lies within this interval estimate, and this is then called a confidence interval.

LONGITUDINAL DATA
See CROSS-SECTIONAL DATA.

NORMAL CURVE
The
Normal curve
looks like this! If
a set of data is drawn
in a stemplot or histogram,
it is surprising how often this
particular shape emerges. The shape
is one whose distribution has a peak in the
middle and is symmetrical with two tails at either side.

In fact the shape is so common that it has been called *Normal*. Note the capital 'N' — not to be confused with the word 'normal'.

NULL HYPOTHESIS
A common activity in Statistics is to test whether two groups of things are noticeably different from each other and this is known as a *Test of Significance*. This test needs to be done in a fairly formal way, so as to ensure that you aren't simply fooling

yourself that there is a difference when there isn't one. The usual approach is to start by assuming that there is no difference, and this is called the *null hypothesis*. You then make the *alternative hypothesis*, which might be that the first group is bigger than the second group. Until proved otherwise, you must assume that the null hypothesis is true.

PLACEBO EFFECT

In the sorts of experiments where a particular treatment is tried out on an experimental group of people, it has been found that some people respond well to the *idea* of getting treatment, regardless of what the treatment contains. This is known as the *placebo effect*, and for this reason it is necessary to give the control group some sort of placebo treatment which is known to be harmless (perhaps a spoonful of distilled water) so that the two groups appear to have been treated in exactly the same way.

SKEWED DISTRIBUTION

Distributions are often symmetrical, but sometimes they are *skewed* to one side like this:

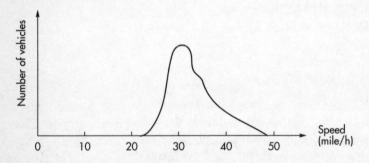

Figure G. 1   The speeds of a sample of vehicles in a 30 mile/h speed limit zone

This particular distribution is described as being 'skewed to the right', because the long tail is on the right-hand side.

SPURIOUS

Spurious means something that isn't what it appears to be. In Statistics it is particularly used along with the words *accuracy* and *correlation*. So, *spurious accuracy* might be giving an answer to seven decimal places when the original data from which the result was calculated were only very rough approximations. *Spurious correlation* is when there is a strong statistical relationship between the things in question, and this is presented as evidence of cause-and-effect when in fact there is not a cause-and-effect relationship.

STANDARD DEVIATION
There are several measures which show how widely spread a set of data is — for example the range, the interquartile range and the mean deviation. By far the most common and useful measure of spread, however, is the *standard deviation*.

STRATIFIED SAMPLING
This is where the population is first divided (stratified) into groups (strata) and then samples are taken from these groups.

TAIL
Most distributions have one or more peaks in the middle and a *tail* at either side.

TEST OF SIGNIFICANCE
See NULL HYPOTHESIS.

UNIMODAL
Unimodal means, literally, 'one mode' and refers to a distribution which has a single peak.

WEIGHTING
Often in Statistics we have to recognise the fact that some values occur more frequently than others. *Weighting* is the term used to describe calculations which take into account these different frequencies — for example, calculating the RPI (see INDEX NUMBER).

Index

The publishers would like to thank the following for their permission to reproduce copyright photographs:

Greenpeace/Perez (cover), Associated Press Ltd (page 59).

British Library Cataloguing in Publication Data
Graham, Alan T. (Alan Thomas) 1947-
    Investigating statistics.
    1. Statistical mathematics
    I. Title
    519.5

    ISBN 0-340-49311-9

First published 1990

Typeset by Keyset Composition, Colchester
Printed in Great Britain for the educational publishing division of Hodder and Stoughton Ltd, Mill Road, Dunton Green, Sevenoaks, Kent by Richard Clay Ltd, Bungay, Suffolk